W9-ASO-540

Books by the Same Author

THE BURNING BUSH

THE UNCONQUERED

THE MAGIC FLIGHT

THE LORE OF THE OLD TESTAMENT

THE LORE OF THE NEW TESTAMENT

HEART UPON THE ROCK (*a novel*)

THE LEGEND CALLED MERYOM (*a novel*)

HOW THE GREAT RELIGIONS BEGAN

MEN AND TREES

FAIR AND WARMER

EVERYBODY'S WEATHER

HOLIDAYS AROUND THE WORLD

YOUNG HEROES OF THE LIVING RELIGIONS

YOUNG HEROES
of the Living Religions

YOUNG HEROES
of the Living Religions

by JOSEPH GAER

Drawings by Anne Marie Jauss

LITTLE, BROWN AND COMPANY
Boston

LIBRARY OF CONGRESS CATALOG CARD NO. 53-7323

FIRST EDITION

Published simultaneously
in Canada by McClelland and Stewart Limited

PRINTED IN THE UNITED STATES OF AMERICA

Introduction

This book tells of twelve youths who, though they lived many centuries ago, are remembered today with even greater love and admiration than during their own times. They were not great warriors in epic battles; nor kings famous for their conquests. These twelve were heroes who started out to find a new and better way of life for men to follow.

The way each found, and the commandments he established to keep men on that way, resulted in a new faith in the purpose of living, called "a religion."

This book tells about the childhood and youth of the founders of the twelve most important living religions in the world today. All these religions have followings, some very large and others quite small. But to each of the followers, his own religion seems best; and its founder is held in the same esteem as other believers have for the founders of their faiths.

When we talk of "living religions" we imply that there were other religions in the world which are now dead. That is really so. The religions of the Babylonians, the

Ancient Greeks, the Chaldeans, the Romans, and the Umbrians are among the many faiths that thrived at one time and then died.

For from time to time the people of certain nations turned from the teachings of their priests, the ceremonies of their churches, and the rituals of their established faith, to accept another faith. This was sometimes done voluntarily, because the teachings of their own faith no longer seemed good in their eyes; more often they were forced to give up their religion by a conqueror who imposed his own faith on the subject peoples.

New faiths were born when certain individuals began to question the beliefs of their ancestors. They asked: even if the priesthood accepted slavery, is slavery right? Are people from birth marked as superior and inferior, as implied in the "caste" system? Is it right for people to work day in, day out, all year round, without a day of rest, even if their ancestors never asked for one? Is man made for the Sabbath or the Sabbath for man? Is justice more important than love, or love greater than justice? Can evil be destroyed by evil, or can only good destroy evil? These, and many other questions like these, were asked. They asked them in private and they asked them in public. And they found people willing to listen.

Their questions irritated the elders and the governors and the priests who demanded obedience without questioning. These tried to silence the questioners and accused them of attempting to destroy God and religion; for they considered anyone who questioned even a single tenet of the established religion an enemy of God.

Great courage is required to challenge an old faith and to preach a new one. People who can do that, whether we agree with them or not, are truly heroes.

The twelve treated in this book were such heroes, who succeeded in establishing new religions. Of course, their fame came after they were mature and, in some cases, old men. In their own times little was known about their childhood and youth. In fact, we know very little about their early days even now.

Only after they were dead and their following increased did the many stories about their early childhood and youth begin to be told. In folk imagination their infancy and youth was imaginatively presented in great adoration. All the love the people felt for them found an outlet in legends about their birth, their infancy, and their youth. These legends, full of wonder and miracles, arose about practically all the founders of the living religions.

This book gives, for the most part, the lore rather than the history. But folklore can be as revealing as history. And the youth and childhood of the founders of the world's living religions, as given in the lore, is as revealing as their teachings, which had such a deep influence on mankind.

Contents

I. VISHNU THE EIGHTH

The Complaint of the Goddess of the Earth

One day, so long ago that it is beyond the memory of man, Basundhara, Goddess of the Earth, appeared on Mount Meru before the gods, Brahma the Creator and Siva the Destroyer.

"I have come to complain about Kangsa, King of Mathura," she said to them. "That harsh tyrant oppresses the people beyond endurance, and there is so much evil on earth that if you do not come to my help, the earth will sink to the lower regions."

After some time of meditation, Brahma said:

"Let us go together to Vishnu the Preserver and present your complaint to him. For Vishnu went down seven times, in the guise of animal or man, to remove evil from the earth; and he might go down an eighth time to preserve mankind."

And so Brahma the Creator, Siva the Destroyer, and Basundhara, Goddess of the Earth, surrounded by many lesser gods, went to the Sea of Milk, where Vishnu the Preserver lay asleep on the back of the great serpent Ananta, and they sang this *mantra* (hymn) to waken him:

You who have the complexion of the Atasi *flower*
And eyes like the petals of the lotus —
You who are charming as the autumn moon
And clothed in yellow and garlanded with flowers —
Favor us!

Vishnu awoke from his slumbers and asked:

"Gods, why are you here?"

Brahma told him of Basundhara's plea for help.

"We have come to you," Brahma concluded, "to ask you to deliver the Earth from her oppressors. Whatever you counsel us to do, we shall humbly obey."

"What you ask is hard, indeed," Vishnu replied. "For it was I who made Kangsa great. And once, I granted him a prayer that none but his cousin's son should have the power to kill him."

Basundhara grieved to hear this and was in despair. Vishnu then plucked two hairs from his body, one white and one black. And he said:

"Grieve not, Basundhara. This white hair will be born as the seventh son of Devaki, Kangsa's cousin. And I myself shall be born out of the black hair as Devaki's eighth son. And I, Kangsa's kin, shall kill the tyrant. But I need Siva's help in this."

"Command me, and it shall be done," said Siva.

"I want your wife Parvati to appear as the infant daughter of Yasoda, the milk-woman of Braja, the moment I am born to Devaki, Kangsa's cousin."

And as Vishnu finished speaking, he disappeared, while the other gods were still bowing to him.

The Birth of Krishna

King Kangsa of Mathura was taking a drive in the royal carriage with his cousin Devaki and her husband Vasudeva at the time the gods met with Vishnu. As they rode along, the king heard a voice from heaven call out:

"Devaki's eighth child shall cause Kangsa's death!"

The king drew his sword and was about to kill his cousin, when Vasudeva caught his arm and pleaded:

"The voice said that her child will kill you, not Devaki. Let her live, my king, and I promise to turn over to you her next child, which shall be her seventh, and any child she may bear after that."

The king spared his cousin's life, but when they returned from their drive he placed a guard around her quarters.

Devaki was kept virtually a prisoner in her quarters until her seventh child was born. Then the news was brought to the king that the child was stillborn. (Actually, the child born of Vishnu's white hair was alive and strong. He was named Balarama by his father and secretly left in the care of a maidservant.)

When Devaki was with child again, the king doubled

the guard over his cousin and her husband. Only trusted midwives were allowed to come near Devaki. And all were instructed to bring the child as soon as it was born directly to the king.

For this was the child the king dreaded.

On the eighth night of the month of Bhadra, Devaki gave birth to her eighth child, and the moment the child was born, a very strange thing happened: everyone in the palace fell into a deep sleep.

Sleep overcame the infant's mother, the midwives and servants, the inner guards and the outer guards, the king and queen, and the courtiers about them. All in the palace lay fast asleep except Vasudeva, the child's father.

Guided by a divine vision, Vasudeva quickly covered his newly born son in wraps and fled with him out of the city to find the house of the cowherd of Braja whose wife, Yasoda, had just given birth to a girl.

On his way, Vasudeva had to cross a broad and turbulent river. The night was dark and a heavy rain fell, and there was not a boat or ferry in sight to take them across the river. Suddenly the father saw a jackal wading into the water, and he followed it, wondering all the while how it was that though the rain fell in torrents, he and his child remained dry. He looked up and saw an enormous snake curving across the river like a hood and sheltering him and the child from the downpour.

Vasudeva soon reached the other side of the river and he hastened to the cowherd's cottage. There he found

Yasoda sleeping with her newly born daughter in her arms. He exchanged the children without waking the mother, and hurried off on his way home.

The guards were still asleep when he reached Devaki's bedside. He placed the milk-woman's child in the crook of his wife's arm, and then the infant began to cry loudly. Everyone in the palace awoke. The guards began to stir and messengers ran to the king to announce that Devaki had just given birth to a girl.

The king ordered the infant brought to him at once, and with his own hands he dashed the child against a stone. But the child, unhurt, rose into the air, and before their very eyes turned into Parvati, Siva's wife. As she rode up to the skies on her lion, she called out to the king:

"Your efforts have been in vain. He who will slay you has been born. Take heed, for you contend not with a man but with the greatest of the gods!"

And with these words she vanished.

When the king realized that he had been deceived, he sent his men out to search for and kill every newly born boy in the land. But he set Devaki and her husband free, not blaming them for what had happened and knowing that there was no further purpose in keeping them prisoners in the palace.

As soon as Vasudeva was freed, he took his seventh son, Balarama, and hurried back to Braja and the cowherd's house. He found the cowherd and his wife happy with the child they assumed to be their own son. Vasudeva asked them to care also for Balarama and to rear him too as their own. This they gladly undertook to do. And in that way Balarama, born of Vishnu's white hair, was destined to grow up with his younger brother, Krishna — a word that means "the black," for Krishna was born of Vishnu's black hair.

The brothers grew to manhood in the forest, playing many pranks, happily caring for their foster parents' cattle, and often frightening the cowherd and his wife by the feats of unnatural strength performed by Krishna.

Indra of the Cows

When Krishna and Balarama were still young boys the cowherds of Braja gathered in great numbers to celebrate the end of the rainy season and to offer up the customary sacrifices to Indra, God of Rain. Krishna, always ready for a prank, turned to the cowherds and asked slyly:

"What is the object of your sacrifices?"

"Indra is the God of the Clouds," they answered. "He gives us rain to grow the crops; and he stops the rains to let the grains grow. We make the sacrifices to show him our gratitude."

"That would be wise for the tillers of the soil," said Krishna. "But we are cowherds. Our livelihood depends on our cattle, who graze in the forests and on the hills. We should rather worship the Gods of the Woods and the

Mountains. For if we do not please them, they will unleash wolves and tigers who will devour our herds. Let us therefore worship the Gods of the Woods and the Hills who dwell in yonder mountain." And Krishna pointed to the lofty mountain Gobardham.

The cowherds took counsel among themselves, and then called together all the cowherds in the land to prepare a great celebration at the foot of the mountain. They brought their cattle and adorned the cows with garlands of flowers. And they invited priests to lead them in the religious rites.

Krishna meanwhile ascended to the top of Gobardham and waited there to see what would happen.

Just as he had expected, Indra, God of Rain, became very angry when he saw the cowherds had turned to worship another god. He commanded the clouds to avenge him against the ungrateful cowherds. The clouds opened up with deafening thunder; lightning slashed across the sky; and great torrents poured down upon the earth. The rain streamed down without ceasing. And soon a great flood threatened to drown the cowherds, their families, and their cattle.

But Krishna put out the little finger of his left hand, lifted the mountain upon it, and held it aloft. All the cowherds, their wives, their children, their cattle and everything they owned came under the mountain and out of the storm. And there they remained dry and secure for seven days and seven nights.

Then the rain stopped and the sun came out. And the cowherds and their families began to wonder about Krishna and his miraculous deeds. They said that Krishna was not a man of mortal birth, but must be a demon or a god.

"I am sorry that you are ashamed of me and are not content to know me as your kinsman," said Krishna. "But I am not a demon and I was born as one of yourselves."

Meanwhile the God of Rain came down from heaven on his elephant to see who it was that had outwitted him. And he found Krishna herding cattle in the forest near Vrindhavan. Except for the dark color of Krishna's skin, there was nothing unusual about the young boy surrounded by his rustic companions. Then Indra looked up and he saw Garuda, half-man and half-bird, floating over Krishna's head. Indra knew that Garuda was the vehicle of the Lord Vishnu the Preserver, greatest of all the gods in heaven. And Indra at once approached Krishna and asked forgiveness for opening the skies and attempting to cause a flood on earth.

"On behalf of the sacred animals you have saved, I thank you!" said Indra. "And henceforth you shall be known as Indra of the Cows."

Indra took a pitcher and sprinkled Krishna with holy water as he named him. And the cows gathered around them began to pour out so much milk that it flowed like a river all around the world.

Indra embraced Krishna in a parting farewell, mounted on his elephant, and rode away to heaven.

Krishna and the Maidens

Though Krishna performed many miraculous deeds and great feats of strength, he lived and behaved like the other cowherds, so that King Kangsa would not learn who he was until the time came for their encounter.

Krishna and his brother Balarama watched over their herds in the pastures; made garlands of wild flowers and wove peacock feathers into their hair; laughed and shouted; and leaped over rocks and fallen logs. And when the day was over, they joined the other cowherds in their evening amusements.

One day Krishna walked along the edge of the River Jumna, when suddenly, from beyond a clump of trees, he heard peals of laughter. Krishna stole to an opening in the thicket and there he saw a group of young women, wives and daughters of the herdsmen, swimming in the river, laughing and splashing each other. Not far from the shore Krishna spied their clothes in a heap.

He crept forward undetected, tied the clothes into a bundle, and took it with him to his hiding place behind a tree. There he waited.

Sometime later, as the young women tired of their sport, they came out of the river. To their great surprise they could find no sign of their garments. They scampered about looking everywhere along the ground, when they heard a flute being played from behind a tree. They looked up in consternation and saw Krishna. The young women screamed in alarm and raced back into the river until the water reached as far as their necks. Then they begged Krishna to return their clothes.

He listened to their pleadings, saying not a word, playing his flute softly and watching their discomfort with amusement.

Then the women threatened to report his conduct to their fathers and their husbands.

"As soon as you get dressed and go home," said Krishna.

"Yes," said the women, crestfallen.

"I will return your clothes," said Krishna, "if you promise to dance with me my favorite dance, the Rāsa-mandala, before you go home."

They promised. And as soon as they were dressed, the young women gathered on a level spot on the bank of the river for the dance.

Then something very strange happened: Though the young women were many, Krishna danced with all of them at the same time. Each woman had her arms around his neck; each one kissed him to make certain that he was real; and each one expressed her devotion to young Krishna, thinking that he was a god who could bring salvation to her soul.

But in all the legends in the Sacred Books about Krishna's pranks on the bathers, it is nowhere mentioned whether the women reported Krishna's conduct to their fathers or their husbands.

Kangsa's Death

Word reached King Kangsa of Mathura that in the Province of Vrindhavan, near Braja, there lived two young cowherds, and the elder was the seventh, and the younger was the eighth son of his cousin Devaki.

The king called one of his trusted nobles and gave him the order to bring the two young cowherds to Mathura.

"The boys are still young, and I have strong men who can destroy them," said the king.

The noble arrived at Braja and was received with due respect by Krishna and Balarama. The brothers set out with him for Mathura, the capital of the kingdom, with open pleasure.

On the way they stopped to bathe in a river. The king's emissary looked at the brothers, and he froze with awe. For he saw the elder brother turn into a thousand-headed serpent, curling up its many coils to make a soft couch for Krishna to rest upon. And Krishna appeared robed in yellow, stretching out four arms, to display on his breast the Crest of Vishnu. But when the nobleman moved his head, the brothers had returned to their cowherd forms. And they proceeded on the journey.

At the gates of Mathura, Balarama and Krishna left the chariot by which they had traveled and entered the city on foot.

The first man they met was the royal laundryman,

carrying a huge bundle of the king's garments. Krishna took the clothes from the frightened washerman and distributed them to the poor herdsmen at the city gate. Then he and his brother went on toward the palace.

As they neared the entrance, a man on a maddened elephant came rushing at them. The driver had orders from the king to ride over the boys and crush them. As the wild beast reached them, Krishna caught hold of its tail, and Balarama caught its trunk. For a while they played with the elephant as they used to play in childhood with the calves. Then Krishna swung the brute about his head, swifter and swifter, and when, finally, he let the animal go, the elephant troubled them no more.

The next day, Kangsa ordered the two brothers taken to the great arena to meet giant wrestlers in contest. Nearly all the populace of Mathura turned out to witness the event, including the entire royal family. Devaki was among the spectators, and when she saw her two sons, she wept with joy that they were alive, and she wept with fear, that they must meet the dreaded giants.

Her fear did not last long. Devaki's sons easily vanquished one giant wrestler after another. The frantic king ordered more and more wrestlers to replace the defeated ones. And he ordered the musicians to stop playing, lest the music encouraged the two boys. The musicians obeyed the royal command to stop playing, yet the music continued and gave courage to the brothers.

Suddenly Krishna rushed at the king, dragged him down from the throne, and began to wrestle with him. He threw Kangsa to the ground and leaned upon him. And as soon as the weight of him who supports and preserves the universe rested on the king, the great weight crushed the soul out of Kangsa. The king was dead.

Krishna arose and before all those assembled in the arena, he restored the throne to Kangsa's father.

Arrow in the Heel

The Lord Vishnu, Supporter and Preserver of the Universe, came down to earth as a cowherd named Krishna to save mankind from the oppression and wickedness of King Kangsa. But he did not return to the Sea of Milk in his heavenly abode as soon as Kangsa was dead. Krishna married sixteen thousand maidens and became the father of one hundred and eighty thousand sons; and his grandchildren were so many that they needed thirty-eight million schools. (This is the way the lore indicates that Krishna is the Father of Mankind.)

The most important part of Krishna's life on earth lasted eighteen days, spent in the most famous battle ever recorded.

In one of the greatest, and by far the longest, epic poems in the world, called the Mahabharata, the record of

Krishna's part in The War of the Five Brothers is given in detail.

The Mahabharata consists of over one hundred and ten thousand stanzas, and is eight times as long as the Iliad and the Odyssey combined. It tells the story of a great struggle that took place for the rule of Northern India between the five brothers of the House of Pandu and their many cousins, the Kurus.

Both the Kurus and the Pandus appealed to Krishna for help. Krishna, wishing to remain impartial, offered to one side an army of one million soldiers and to the other side he offered himself, not as a fighter but as an adviser in battle. The Kurus took the army, and the Pandus took Krishna, who became charioteer for their general, Arjuna.

During the battle that lasted eighteen days Arjuna became full of doubt, and he asked Krishna about life and death. When Krishna replied, Arjuna cried out:

"My bewilderment has vanished away; I stand free from doubt; I will do as you command me!"

The discussion between Krishna and Arjuna on the field of battle as recorded in the Mahabharata is known as the Bhagavad-Gita, and is the most famous of all Hindu poems.

After the wars, Krishna and his brother Balarama settled in Dwaraka. And there Krishna wandered in the woods one day, deep in contemplation. When he tired, he sat down on the bare ground in the attitude of yoga, which is the attitude of one meditating on the Supreme Spirit, and this posture exposed the bare sole of his foot. A hunter came by and, mistaking Krishna for a deer, shot an arrow into Krishna's foot. Krishna died of the wound, his mission on earth having been completed.

The Lord's Song (Bhagavad-Gita)

There are about three hundred million people, mainly in India, who believe in a religion called Brahminism or Hinduism, which is the oldest of all the living religions. Hinduism has not remained the same throughout the many centuries. It has changed. And the Sacred Books, the ritual, and the sacred legends, have kept growing in size and number. (One of these books, for example, states in the beginning that its length is 8800 stanzas or couplets; but the work as we have it today contains more than 110,000 stanzas. Clearly, something has been added since this work was first undertaken.)

The Oldest of the Hindu Sacred Books are the Vedas. These are poetic collections of hymns, magic spells, and sacrifices to the gods. The Vedas present the story of Creation, the nature of life, the rule of Heaven and Earth, the rise of the different castes among men, and how man ought to serve the gods and find redemption.

In time three great prose works were added to the Vedas. These are: The Brahmanas, Aranyakas, and the Upanishads.

It is as difficult to sum up briefly the great teachings of

the Vedas and the added books, as it would be to sum up the eighty books of the Bible. But it is important to point out that in the Upanishads we already find clearly expressed the Law of Life, called Karma, which is the central doctrine of Hinduism. The Brihadaranyaka Upanishad states simply:

"A man of good acts will become good, a man of bad acts, bad. He becomes pure by pure deeds, bad by bad deeds. And here they say that a man consists of desires. And as is his desire, so is his will; and as is his will, so is his deed; and whatever deed he does, that he will reap."

Later two great epic works were added to the Vedas, just as the Apocrypha were added to the Bible.

The first of these epics is called Ramayana, a work in seven volumes, which presents the exciting story of the trials, struggles and triumphs of Prince Rama, who was in reality the Seventh Incarnation of the God Vishnu, the Preserver.

The second epic is the Mahabharata, which we have already described as devoted to the Bharata Wars for the control of Northern India. In this epic the discussion on the battlefield between Krishna and the general, Arjuna, known as the Bhagavad-Gita (The Lord's Song), is often shortened to the Gita.

The Gita, about as long as the Book of Job in our Bible, is probably the best known and the most important part of all the Hindu Scriptures.

There are literally enough legends about Krishna to fill

a library — how he came to earth as Devaki's son; how he lived as a cowherd in Braja; his many pranks; his encounter with Indra, God of Rain; his numerous contests before killing the demon-king Kangsa; and his adventures in the Bharata Wars and after.

A number of the events in Krishna's life are observed in feasts throughout India; and of these the Birth of Krishna, the Janmashtami, is a holiday that compares with the celebration of Christmas among Christians.

The Hindus never tire of telling the stories about Krishna, and these are narrated in a prescribed form, each tale ending with:

"So, all you who have listened to this sacred story, cry victory to Vishnu — ulu! ulu! ulu!"

But Krishna is so well remembered, not for any of the exploits narrated in these sacred tales, but for the unforgettable discourse on the immortality of the soul as given in the Bhagavad-Gita, The Lord's Song.

II. PRINCE SIDDHARTHA GAUTAMA

The Unhappy King and Queen

Many, many centuries ago, the Kingdom of the Sakyas, at the foot of the Himalaya Mountains, was ruled by the good King Suddhodana and his queen, Maya.

The king was loved by his people, for he was as brave as he was just. And Queen Maya was even more beloved. Queen Maya, the people said, was as beautiful as the Queen of Heaven. Her voice was sweeter than the song of birds in spring; her eyes were lovelier than the blue lotus; her hair was blacker and silkier than the black bee; and her features had the grace of Lakshmi, Goddess of Good Fortune. Even greater than her beauty were her goodness, her humility and her kindness.

Yet the good king and his beautiful queen were unhappy in their palace in Kapilavastu, for though they had been married for many years, they had no children. And Suddhodana, the son of a king, the grandson of a king, and the great-grandson of a king, feared that with him would end the dynasty of rulers that went back to the beginning of the Sakya kingdom.

Maya's Dream

One day Queen Maya appeared before her husband, radiant as the Queen of the Zodiac, and said:

"My lord, I have come to ask of you a great favor."

"Speak, my beloved," said the king. "For your wish is my command."

"I wish to retire to the tower of our palace, from this day forward to live in austerity; fasting, and denying myself all worldly comforts and desires."

The king kept his word and granted her wish. And Maya dwelt like a daughter of the gods in the tower of the palace, where no man was allowed to enter.

In the third year of the queen's retirement, on the night when spring was born, Maya dreamt a marvelous dream. She dreamt that as she was gazing up toward the starlit heavens the skies opened and out of them came down a young elephant with six snow-white tusks.

At that moment thirty-two good omens appeared in the world and lasted for as long as Maya was asleep. The lame could walk. The hungry were sated. Horses neighed and elephants trumpeted gently. All musical instruments began to play of their own accord. The salt waters of the oceans turned sweet. Flowers bloomed out of season. The skies were clear, yet rain fell. The earth became covered with lotus of different colors. All men spoke gently. All women were kindly. And thousands of gods came down to the sleeping Maya and sang their celestial songs.

Maya awoke, happier than she had ever been. For she understood the meaning of her dream. She dressed at once in her most dazzling robes, left the tower of the palace for the royal garden, and seated herself in the shadow of a Varana tree.

"Go to the king," she said to her maid, "and tell him that I wish to see him here."

King Suddhodana, who had not seen the queen for thirty-two months, ran into the garden, eager to see her.

"My beloved, you sent for me!"

"I have dreamt a dream, my lord," said the queen. "And I wish you would send for the Brahmans who know the meaning of dreams and who can tell us whether the palace has been visited by the gods for good or for evil."

The Brahmans were summoned, and when they heard her dream, they exclaimed:

"Blessed are you, Maya, above all mothers! For you shall give birth to a son who will be the favorite of all the gods."

King Suddhodana ordered gifts distributed to all the poor in his kingdom; and to all the women in his domain were sent flowers and perfume.

The news that a white elephant with six tusks had descended as a messenger from heaven, and that Queen Maya would soon give birth to a son, traveled like lightning throughout the Kingdom of the Sakyas; and people streamed to Kapilavastu to ask the queen's blessings. A blade of grass plucked by Queen Maya and given to a dying man brought him back to health again. And whomsoever Maya touched — the sick, the deaf, the dumb, and the blind — each was cured and whole again.

During all the time Maya awaited the birth of her son, a sweet melody was heard over the palace, carried on the wings of a breeze; and showers of fragrant flowers fell over the palace and the royal city of Kapilavastu.

Asita's Prophecy

When the time arrived for Maya to give birth to her son, her maids carried her on a magnificent palanquin out of the palace grounds and into the woods. They were preceded by musicians in bright garments, adorned with precious stones and ropes of pearls, and they were followed by beautiful maidens, singing the songs that delight Sarasati, Goddess of the Muses.

In the woods the queen alighted. She left her companions behind and drew the branch of a tree in bloom down over her. The leaves at once intertwined and the branch turned into a partition that shielded her as if she were in a private chamber.

Suddenly the earth trembled. The air around the world became filled with a light so clear that even the darkest caverns were flooded with brilliant light. All the trees on earth blossomed and their fruit ripened out of season. And four sons of the gods appeared to receive the infant. They placed him in his mother's arms, saying:

"Rejoice, lady, for great is the son that was born to you!"

Word was immediately carried to King Suddhodana. And the king, surrounded by wise Brahmans, came to see the child. When they reached the woods, they saw the newly born infant standing on his own feet before his mother and facing north. The king and the holy men bowed before the child.

"I name you Siddhartha Gautama," said the king to his son, "for you, a descendant of the Sakyas, will fulfill the promises that have been foretold about you before you were born."

While the Brahmans foretold great things about Prince Siddhartha, an aged hermit in the high mountains, the great seer Asita, saw the bright spirits of heaven rejoicing. He asked them for the cause of their happiness. And they told him of the birth of Siddhartha, who had come to bring joy to the world.

The aged Asita left Himavat, the holy mountain on which he dwelt, and made his way to Kapilavastu and the palace of the king, where he asked to see the prince.

The king received the aged seer with great honor and brought him to the chamber of the queen and her child. The old man looked long at the infant in his mother's arms, and then Asita began to weep.

"Tell me," asked the king anxiously, "do you foresee danger to our son?"

"I weep for myself, not your son," said the hermit. "For I foresee that he will live the holy life and reach perfection. He will bring enlightenment to the world. But I am old. And I weep that I shall not live to the day when he will become the Burden-Bearer of Mankind."

Asita returned to Mount Himavat; and the king brooded over the bittersweet prophecy of the great seer. For if Asita's prophecy was true, then Prince Siddhartha would renounce his kingdom and become the Buddha, the Enlightened One, and the throne of the Sakyas would be filled by another. Also, if the prince was to become the Buddha, then his mother, as had been decreed since the beginning of time, must ascend to the sky and take her place among the gods, seven days after the birth of her child.

The king called in many Brahman soothsayers and astrologers to tell him what they could see in the stars.

The Brahmans deliberated, and they examined the mother and the child. Finally they said to the king:

"Queen Maya has all the signs of the mother of the Buddha; and Prince Siddhartha has every one of the thirty-two marks of the Great Man."

"What are the thirty-two marks of the Great Man?" asked the king.

"He was born with forty teeth. His eyes are intensely blue. He has the eyelashes of a cow, and the jaw of a lion.

Between his eyebrows appears a mole of white down. His proportions have the symmetry of the banyan tree: the compass of his arms equals his height. His frame is divinely straight. His skin is so delicately smooth that no dust can cleave to his body. His complexion is the color of gold. His legs are like the antelope's. His ankles are like rounded shells. His fingers and his toes are long, and the palms of his hands and the soles of his feet are soft and tender. His heels are projecting. When he stands upright, his hands can touch his knees. And his voice is as sweet as the voice of the Karavika bird that lives in the Himalayas. These are some of the thirty-two signs of the Great Man. And your son has all of them."

"And what do you foresee for my son?" asked the king.

"Two roads lie before him. If he follows the road of the royal house, he will become Lord of the Wheel, Ruler of the Right, Conqueror of the four quarters of the earth, and owner of the Seven Treasures. There will be none like him among the Kings of the Earth. But if he follows the road of the homeless ones and the seekers after truth, he will become the Supreme Buddha who will roll back the veil of the world. He will become the Enlightened One."

"What will determine my son which road to follow?" asked the king anxiously.

"Four things will determine whether he shall follow the road of the homeless: an old man, a sick man, a corpse, and a hermit."

The king endowed the Brahmans with many gifts. But

in his heart he determined to keep his son on the path of the royal house.

The Shadow That Did Not Move

Queen Maya died when her child was seven days old, as had been foretold; and Prince Siddhartha was placed in the care of her younger sister, Mahaprajapati. She looked after all the child's wants just as if she were his mother; and the boy grew like a rising sun.

Everyone in the Kingdom of the Sakyas delighted in bringing gifts to amuse the prince. They brought toy elephants and deer, horses and chariots, birds and fish. The poor brought toys made of wood and clay; and the rich brought toys made of gold, studded with rare gems. But the child seemed to play with all of them equally little. For he seemed always absorbed in his own thoughts.

One day Mahaprajapati said to the king: "The time has come for us to take Siddhartha to a teacher, for he is five years old and should be instructed in the art of writing and the skill of reading."

The king agreed, and he took his son to the learned holy man, Visvanitra. When the prince was seated before his teacher with a tablet of gilded sandalwood, he asked:

"Which of the sixty-four different scripts in the world do you wish me to learn, master?" And he named all the scripts and described their peculiarities and differences.

Then the prince added: "The vowel 'A' in all of them is sounded as in the word *anitya;* the vowel 'I' is sounded as in the word *indriya;* and the vowel 'U' is sounded as in the word *upagupta.*"

The astonished Visvanitra said to the child: "You, my Prince, have been brought to be taught by me. Yet you have mentioned scripts, the names of which I do not know. It is I rather who should sit at your feet and learn."

Upon leaving Visvanitra, the young prince wandered off by himself into a meadow. The noonday sun was hot and he walked into the shade of a clump of trees. There he sat down and was soon lost in meditation.

At the palace the child was missed and no one could find him. The king sent servants out in all directions to look for the prince, and they searched for him all afternoon. At the end of the day one servant returned out of breath and reported:

"My lord! I have found him! I have found the prince!"

"But where is he?" asked the king. "Why didn't you bring him to me? Is he well?"

"He is well, my lord, but I dared not disturb him. I found him sitting in the shadow of a tree, meditating. And then I noticed something very strange, and I dared not move toward him. For all the shadows of the trees had lengthened with the passing of the day, but the shadow of the tree under which the prince meditated had not moved."

The king's happiness that his son had been found unhurt

was mixed with sadness in the recollection of what the Brahmans had foretold about the road of the homeless that his son might follow, and the four sights that would lead him to it. And the king began to think of ways in which he might keep his son from seeing those sights.

The Three Palaces of Distraction

King Suddhodana ordered three palaces to be built: a palace of spring, a palace of summer, and a palace of winter. And between them was to be planted a Garden of Happiness.

After several years the palaces were ready, and they were the most beautiful ever built on earth. Each palace had many pavilions leading in all directions, through richly ornamented porticoes. The great halls inside were surrounded by delicately carved galleries; and the ceilings rose in ornamented domes. The pagodas and the turrets of the palaces rose like golden fingers reaching for the sky. And on each of the pagodas a thousand silver bells tinkled softly in the breeze.

Around the palaces were the lakes and pools of the Garden of Happiness, fringed by the rarest of trees and flowers. The air was filled with the scent of jasmine and the sound of the singing swans, gliding among the blue lotus of the pools.

And all about the garden and the palaces rose great

walls, constructed to keep out the world of sickness and sorrow.

For the king it was a day of happiness when the three palaces of distraction were completed, and he ordered a chariot to take Prince Siddhartha to dwell there until the time came for him to take over the rule of the kingdom. All along the way a guard of honor was stationed, and the road was strewn with flowers.

As the chariot passed along the festive road, they came upon a very old man, leaning heavily on a cane, his skin wrinkled, his sight dim, his teeth chattering.

The prince turned to the driver and asked: "What ails this man?"

"He is suffering from old age," answered the driver.

"Is it a peculiarity of his family?" asked the prince, who had never seen an old man before.

"It is a peculiarity of all mankind," said the driver. "Your own father and even you will end in old age."

"Then youth is vain and the pleasures of youth are vain," said the prince. "Turn around and let us go home!"

The king realized unhappily that part of the prohecy had come true. But he persuaded his son to go back to the Three Palaces of Distraction. And this time the king ordered even greater precaution along the road.

But on the way the prince's chariot passed a man whose limbs were withered and who could hardly breathe.

"What ails this man?" asked the prince.

"He is ill," replied the driver. "Illness is no respecter of persons, and may attack a king as well as a beggar. That is a condition of living."

"Then health is vain; and the wise man refrains from indulgence and pleasures," said the prince. "Turn around and let us go home!"

The unhappy king once again prevailed upon his son to go to the Garden of Happiness. And he ordered precautions over every foot of the road.

This time the prince's chariot was stopped by a funeral procession. The bier was surrounded by wailing women and followed by a drummer and a flutist playing a mournful tune.

"What are they carrying that makes them so unhappy?" asked the prince.

"A dead man, my prince," said the driver. "Though they mourn and weep, he cannot hear them. For this is Death that awaits all men."

"If such is the end of man, how idle are all his pleasures," said the prince. "Turn around and let us go home!"

A fourth time the king urged his son to go and dwell in the Garden of Happiness. This time he ordered a chain of guards sixteen miles long to keep out of sight any of the infirm, the aged, and the dead.

Again the prince's chariot started out. But after a short while they came upon a man carrying a beggar's bowl. He wore an ocher-red cowl, and in his gentle face there was calm, and in his bearing there was peace.

"Who is that man of peaceful mien?" asked the prince.

"He is a bhikshu, a holy beggar, who has left behind his family and all his possessions to seek the divine vision and to listen for the divine voice," said the driver.

King Suddhodana was greatly upset when he heard of the meeting with the holy man, but he still hoped to change the fate foretold for his son. He filled the palaces with glittering dancers and sweet singers, and arranged that at every turn there was music and merriment. At each gate of the garden he placed five hundred armed guards. And he commanded Mahaprajapati to see that the prince was forever enchanted in the joy about him.

Siddhartha's Bride

One day Siddhartha's father came to him and said: "My son, you are now at the age when you ought to think of marriage. Is there anyone who has won your affection?"

The prince replied: "The trees in the forest of desire have their roots in the valley of pain. And there is no maid that has won my affection."

"What rare merits do you expect of the girl who will be your wife?" asked the king.

"The girl I would marry must be beautiful, yet not proud of her beauty. She must be truthful, but not haughty. She must have a sister's affection and a mother's tenderness for all living things. Wine and sweets would not tempt her. Nor would she covet anything belonging to others. She must be humble, but not servile. And she must be pure in body, in speech, and in thought."

"I shall send out the palace Brahman to find a girl that has all these virtues," said the king.

The Brahman traveled all over the Kingdom of the Sakyas, and finally returned to announce that Dandapani of the Sakyas had a daughter named Gopa, worthy of being the prince's wife.

The king decided to test the girl first. And he sent out a royal herald to announce in the streets of Kapilavastu that seven days hence Prince Siddhartha would present gifts to all the young maidens of marriageable age in the city, and to command them to appear on that day at the palace.

On the day announced, the prince sat on the throne presenting gifts to the girls as they passed. Most of them dared not lift their eyes to the prince, and in their excitement dropped the gifts to the floor. The last to appear was Gopa. She approached the prince fearlessly, and looked straight at him. The prince looked about him for a gift, but there were none left.

"In what way have I offended you that you have no gift for me?" asked Gopa.

"You have not offended me," said the prince. He took off his ring and held it out toward her. "Please accept my ring."

"No," said Gopa. "It is rather for me to give you a jewel."

After she left, the prince told the king that Gopa alone had won his affection.

But Gopa's father, Dandapani, announced that his daughter could not marry the prince. For he had vowed that his child would marry a man skillful in the arts, brave in contests of strength, and wise in the sciences.

"Your son," said he to the king, "is famous only for his indolence and contemplation."

The prince then ordered a contest to be held in the art of numbers and writing, and in all skills with horses and elephants, and with bow and arrow. On the day of the contest, the many young noblemen who took part were quickly vanquished by the prince. And at the end Siddhartha asked for an ancient bow and arrow which rested in a temple of the gods.

The prince sent the ancient arrow far beyond the sight of the spectators, and those who followed it found that the arrow had pierced its target at a very great distance, and at the point where it dropped to the ground a fountain of water gushed forth from the spot. They named the fountain, the Well of the Arrow.

Then they placed the victorious prince upon a white elephant and led him to his prize, the beautiful Gopa.

The Buddha: The Enlightened One

The many stories about the infancy and youth of Prince Siddhartha Gautama (and there are hundreds of them) arose long after he became the Buddha: the Enlightened One, long after his teachings became established as a great religion in the world.

After Siddhartha married Gopa and after they had a son, at the time when the prince was twenty-nine years old, he again encountered the four omens: the Sick, the Aged, the Dead, and the Monk.

The prince went to the king and told him of his resolve to become a beggar-monk.

The father pleaded with his son to change his mind. He offered to abdicate and let Siddhartha become King of the Sakyas in his stead.

"I will do as you say," said the prince, "if you will promise me four things."

"What are those four things, my son?"

"Promise me that I shall never meet with misfortune; that I will never grow old; that illness will never threaten me; and that I shall never die."

"These things I cannot promise you," said his father sadly.

"Then I must keep to my resolve and go out in search of understanding until I know where illness and death and human misfortune come from."

And very soon afterwards Siddhartha left home one night on his favorite horse, Kanthaka. He rode through the night until he reached the borders of the Mogadah Kingdom. There he dismounted, shaved his head, put on the garb of a beggar-monk, and began his long pilgrimage in search of the Truth of Life.

Siddhartha's pilgrimage went on for seven years. And then he sat down under a fig tree one day, determined not to leave the place until he had gained the wisdom he sought. After some time his face lit up with joy.

The tree under which he sat has since been named the Bo Tree, the Tree of Wisdom.

The night he spent meditating under the Bo Tree is called The Sacred Night.

And the wisdom he gained is called the Enlightenment.

Ever since that night Prince Siddhartha Gautama has been called the Buddha: the Enlightened One.

After that night he went out into the world to teach the Eightfold Path, or the Eight Rules of Life:

Right Belief — that Truth is the guide of Man;
Right Resolve — never to harm any living thing;
Right Speech — never to lie, never to slander, never to swear;
Right Behavior — never to steal or kill, or to do anything a man might later regret;
Right Occupation — never to seek a livelihood in occupations such as forgery, usury, or the like;
Right Effort — to strive after good and shun evil;
Right Contemplation — to be master of one's thoughts in joy and in sorrow;

Right Concentration — the stage of peace gained by following these rules.

At the age of eighty years the Buddha died near Kushinagara, not far from his birthplace. But his teachings lived on and thrived; and they traveled thousands of miles and found followers over half the length of the earth.

The Jatakas

The followers of the Buddha believe that when the soul of man leaves the sick or aged body, it enters another, newly born body. It is reincarnated.

When it was decided in heaven that the Buddha should appear on earth to teach mankind the way to the Good Life, it was agreed that his soul should first be born in many forms, so that he would come to know all the problems of life and teach the world great wisdom while he was still the Bodisat, which is the name given to the one destined to become the Buddha.

One of the sacred books of the Buddhist, called The Book of the 550 Jatakas (Jatakatthavannana), gives the Birth Stories of the Bodisat before he became the Enlightened One: the Buddha. During the many incarnations, the future Buddha appeared on earth many times as a king, or a prince, or a god, or a slave. Twice he appeared as a thief; and once as a gambler. And many times he appeared as an animal: a lion, a deer, an eagle, a bull, a snake, and so on.

But whatever the form he took, he always took it toward a purpose. And the Jatakas demonstrate that purpose by a given incident or story which teaches a Buddhist lesson.

Here are two tales as they appear in the *Buddhist Birth-Stories (Jataka Tales)*, and as translated from the original Pali by T. W. Rhys Davids:

The Talkative Tortoise

Once upon a time, while Brahma-datta was reigning in Benares, the future Buddha was born in a minister's family; and when he grew up, he became the king's adviser in things temporal and spiritual.

Now this king was very talkative: while he was speaking, others had no opportunity for a word. And the future Buddha, wanting to cure this talkativeness of the king, was constantly seeking for some means of doing so.

At that time there was living in a pond in the Himalaya Mountains a tortoise. Two young hangas (wild ducks), who came to feed there, made friends with him. And one day, when they had become very intimate with him, they said to the tortoise:

"Friend Tortoise! The place where we live, at the Golden Cave on Mount Beautiful in the Himalaya country, is a delightful spot. Will you come there with us?"

"But how can I get there?"

"We can take you, if you can hold your tongue, and will say nothing to anybody."

"O! That I can do! Take me with you!"

"That's right," said they. And making the tortoise bite hold of a stick, they themselves took the two ends in their teeth, and flew up into the air.

Seeing him thus carried by the hangas, some villagers called out: "Two wild ducks are carrying a tortoise along on a stick!" Whereupon the tortoise wanted to say, "If my friends choose to carry me, what is that to you, you wretched slaves!" So just as the swift flight of the wild ducks had brought him over the king's palace in the city of Benares, he let go of the stick he was biting, and falling in the open courtyard, split in two! And there arose a universal cry, "A tortoise has fallen in the open courtyard, and has split in two!"

The king, taking the future Buddha, went to the place, surrounded by his courtiers; and looking at the tortoise, he asked the Bodisat, "Teacher! How comes he to be fallen here?"

The future Buddha thought to himself, "Long expecting, wishing to admonish the king, have I sought for some means of doing so. This tortoise must have made friends with the wild ducks; and they must have made him bite hold of the stick, and had flown him up into the air to take him to the hills. But he, being unable to hold his tongue when he heard anyone else talk, must have wanted to say something, and let go of the stick; and so must have fallen down from the sky, and thus lost his life." And saying, "Truly, O king! those who are called chatterboxes — people whose words have no end — come to grief like this," he uttered these verses:

"Verily the tortoise killed himself
Whilst uttering his voice;
Though he was holding tight the stick,
By a word himself he slew.

Behold him, O excellent by strength!
And speak wise words, not out of season.
You see how, by his talking overmuch,
The tortoise fell into his wretched plight!"

The king saw he was himself referred to, and said, "O teacher! Are you speaking of me?"

And the Bodisat spoke openly, and said: "O great king! Be it thou, or be it any other, whoever talks beyond measure meets with some mishap like this."

And the king henceforth refrained himself, and became a man of few words.

The Ass in the Lion's Skin

Once upon a time, while Brahma-datta was reigning in Benares, the future Buddha was born of a peasant family; and when he grew up, he gained his living by tilling the ground.

At that time a hawker used to go from place to place, trafficking in goods carried by an ass. Now at each place he came to, when he took the pack down from the ass's back, he used to clothe him in a lion's skin, and turn him loose in the rice and barley fields. And when the watchmen in the fields saw the ass, they dared not go near him, taking him for a lion.

One day the hawker stopped in a village; and whilst he was getting his own breakfast cooked, he dressed the ass in a lion's skin, and turned him loose in a barley field. The watchmen in the field dared not go up to to him; but going home, they announced the news. Then all the villagers came out with weapons in their hands; and blowing chanks, and beating drums, they went near the field and shouted. Terrified with the fear of death, the ass uttered a cry — the cry of an ass!

And when he knew him then to be an ass, the future Buddha pronounced the first stanza:

"This is not a lion's roaring,
Nor a tiger's, nor a panther's;
Dressed in a lion's skin,
'Tis a wretched ass that roars!"

But when the villagers knew the creature to be an ass, they beat him till his bones broke; and, carrying off the lion's skin, went away. Then the hawker came; and seeing his ass fallen into so bad a plight, pronounced the second stanza:

"Long might the ass,
Clad in a lion's skin,
Have fed on the barley green,
But he brayed!
And that moment he came to ruin."

And even whilst he was yet speaking the ass died on the spot!

The Four Truths

One in every four people on earth today is a Buddhist, a follower of the Teachings of the Buddha. The majority of the people of China and Japan, Ceylon, Burma and Siam, Tibet, Nepal, and Eastern Turkestan are Buddhists. And small groups of the followers of this religion are to be found in every part of the world, including the United States.

The teachings of Buddhism begin with the belief that there is no Creator of the World, but that the world always was and always will be. This Eternal World is ruled by the Law of Life, which is: *From Good must come Good, and from Evil must come Evil.* In order to live the Good Life, man must grasp the Four Noble Truths:

That life is full of suffering;

That suffering is caused by desire;

That the suppression of desire will abolish suffering;

That the way to suppress desire is not to follow any

extremes of self-denial or self-indulgence, but to find the middle path, which consists of: Right Belief; Right Resolve; Right Speech; Right Behavior; Right Occupation; Right Effort; Right Contemplation; and Right Concentration.

Many, many books have been written to explain these Four Noble Truths. But not all the Buddhist monks and religious leaders agree on their meaning. And today there are many Buddhist sects, each with its own interpretations of the Teachings of Buddhism.

Yet they all start out with the teachings of their great religious leader, who was born over 2500 years ago. Some people believe that the Buddha was the Ninth Incarnation of Vishnu the Preserver, just as Krishna was Vishnu's Eighth Incarnation. He was born in a royal palace, but renounced all claims to his father's kingdom and became the Enlightened One: the Buddha.

III. MAHAVIRA: The Great Hero

King Sreyama's Son

In Northern India, not far from the region where the epic battles of the Mahabharata were fought at the dawn of time, there lived a king named Sreyama, who ruled over the small Kingdom of Mogadah. King Sreyama had little time for affairs of state, for his days were devoted to the study of the Vedas and other sacred books.

He often thought: "If I were not born a king, I would have chosen to be a beggar devoted to contemplation in solitude in the forest."

When the king's first son was born he eagerly assembled all the holy men in his kingdom to foretell the child's future. The holy men prophesied that the prince would grow up a worthy successor to his father.

The king gave a great feast for the heir to his kingdom. And in his heart he prayed for another son who would follow the life of a monk.

Within a year his queen, Trisala, gave birth to another boy. Again the king invited the holy men to foretell the child's future.

"Your son," said one of the sages, "will grow up to

greatness. He will distinguish himself with the horse and the elephant, the bow and the arrow; but greater still will be his understanding of the Sacred Books. For he will add a measure to knowledge; and he will add new meaning to devotion. Whatever he does will please the Thirty-three Gods in Heaven."

The king rejoiced in this prophecy. He gave a great feast for the holy men and all his subjects. And at the feast he named his second son, Vardhamana.

The guests at the christening feast toasted King Sreyama and Queen Trisala, saying:

"May Prince Vardhamana bring us a measure of new knowledge and a new meaning of devotion!"

Almost as early as he learned to walk, Prince Vardhamana showed skill in archery and riding; and almost as early as he learned to talk, he surprised his elders with his knowledge of letters.

The king assigned learned men to teach his younger son all that could be learned from books; and he selected masters to teach him horsemanship, the mastery of elephants, and other skills. Every time the young prince was taught one thing, he proceeded to demonstrate the next thing that would follow, proving himself always one step ahead of his teachers.

The Prince and the Elephant

One day, when the prince was five or six or seven years old, he was playing in the royal garden with the children of the palace. They were all absorbed in their game until suddenly a heavy crashing sound, like thunder, came rolling toward them. The children looked up in terror and saw a maddened old elephant bearing down upon them, his powerful trunk swinging like a weapon of destruction.

The children dashed behind trees screaming in fear. But Vardhamana remained standing quietly in the path of the enraged animal. When the elephant was almost upon him, Vardhamana nimbly caught hold of the swinging trunk and in a swift leap climbed to the animal's head. Then he drove the old bull back to the elephant corral from which he had escaped, and the keepers of the royal animals quickly chained him.

The prince said nothing to his parents of the incident. But the children and the animal trainers came running to the palace, each giving his version of the prince's feat.

King Sreyama proudly put his arms around his son's shoulders and said: "The sages predicted at your birth that there would be no fear in your heart. They were right. I shall therefore rename you *Mahavira*, meaning 'The Great Hero.' "

And after that day Prince Vardhamana of Mogadah was

known to everyone as Mahavira. In time they even forgot his given name. But they never forgot Mahavira, the Great Hero.

The Three Laws

At the age of twelve, Mahavira put on the Sacred Thread of Hinduism, and he was sent to learned Brahmans to be taught the Sacred Books. Of all their teachings Mahavira pondered longest over the Three Laws of Life.

The First Law of Life, he learned, was *Karma Marga:* the Law of the Deed.

From good must come good and from evil must come evil, said the teachers. He who wishes to secure the happiness of heaven must always do good to others, no matter what others do to him.

The Second Law of Life was *Bhaki Marga:* the Law of Love.

The good man, the teachers said, repays love with love and devotion with devotion; and he also repays hatred with love and treachery with devotion.

The Third Law of Life is *Gyana Marga:* the Law of Knowledge.

For without knowledge one cannot tell good from evil; without knowledge one cannot distinguish love from hatred and devotion from treachery; and without knowledge one cannot come to know the Universal Soul, the Brahm, from which all spirits and souls arise.

"Which is greater," Mahavira asked his teachers, "good deeds, knowledge, or love?"

The Brahmans could explain the Laws of Life to him, but they could not tell him which was greater.

Mahavira asked many more questions that his teachers could not answer. And when he asked whether all of life is sacred, they became confused. Their answer was "yes" and yet they ate meat and believed in animal sacrifices to the gods.

Mahavira turned to the Sacred Tales in the holy books to find answers to his many questions.

The Fowler and the Pigeon

In the Mahabharata the young prince found a story that he read with great attention:

Once upon a time there was a wicked fowler who earned his livelihood by snaring pigeons and other birds and selling their meat for food. Though in the course of years he had killed many innocent creatures, the fowler himself never considered his occupation evil.

One day a great storm came on while the fowler was out hunting in the forest. Indra, the God of Rain, had opened all the clouds and it seemed as if the world would soon be destroyed in a flood. The frightened fowler began to look around for shelter. As he plunged through the water he came upon a female pigeon, paralyzed from cold. Though soaked to the skin and fearful of his safety, the fowler could still think of nothing but his usual occupation, and bagged the poor pigeon in his cage.

At that moment he saw a great tree with branches so mighty that it seemed as if the Creator had planted it there especially to protect his creatures in distress. The fowler dashed under the shelter of the tree, set down his cage, and stretched out upon the wet ground, with a stone as his pillow. As he lay there, hungry and cold, he prayed to the gods to spare his life.

This great tree, with mighty spreading branches, was the home of the pigeon in the fowler's cage. She had left her nest earlier to find food for her family, and her mate was now anxiously waiting for her. He sat in the branches listening to the storm and grieving aloud:

"Oh, my dear, what a dreadful storm you are exposed to and I unable to help you! How shall I live if anything has happened to you? What is my life without you? And you were always so good to me! You rejoiced when I rejoiced; and you tried to cheer me up when I was sad. If anger stirred me, you tried to calm me; and when I was away from home you were lonely until I returned. You were my greatest treasure and my best companion. How shall I live without you?"

The pigeon wept when she heard her mate's lament, and she cried out from the cage that she was alive and a blessed wife to have such a devoted husband. She said to him:

"Look upon the wretched fowler under the tree, as if he were at the door of your house. See how he perishes from hunger and cold. It is your duty as his host to save him, for there is no greater duty than hospitality. Save him, even if you must pay with your life for it!"

The male pigeon aroused the fowler and asked what service he could render him. And the fowler replied:

"I am perishing from cold. Can you build a fire to warm me?"

The pigeon gathered dry leaves and twigs and started a fire. As soon as the fowler was warm, he said:

"I am perishing from hunger. Can you get me some food?"

"Alas, we pigeons do not store any food but live from day to day. But you can eat me to save your life."

And without a moment's hesitation he flew into the flames.

The fowler jumped to his feet, stricken with repentance. He saw all at once how evil his entire life had been. And he realized how much better it is to sacrifice one's own life even for the welfare of an enemy, rather than to take the life of the innocent.

He immediately released the female pigeon from the cage and threw away his nets, traps, and arrows. He resolved to spend the rest of his days in repentance as a hermit, preaching that all of life is holy and no one has the right to the life of another.

As the fowler was making his resolution, the female pigeon cast herself into the fire to join her husband. At that moment the sky lit up and a chariot came down to take the pigeon and his wife up to heaven.

Mahavira read on to the end of the story, where it said:

"A person should never do to others what he does not like others to do to him, knowing how painful it is to himself." (Mahabharata: XII, 259:19)

This, said the student prince to himself, is the answer to my question: All life is sacred. One must never injure anything that has a soul. It is evil to make sacrifices of living things. It is evil to eat meat. It is evil to hunt and to fish and to kill even the least of living things wantonly. War is evil. It is evil to fight back an attacker. It is evil to kill a bee or a mosquito even though it stings you. It is evil to step on a worm by the roadside heedlessly, for even the worm has a soul.

Remember *Ahimsa*

Mahavira returned from his studies and settled into a very happy life in the palace. But some time afterwards, when his parents died, Mahavira left his home and lived like a beggar in the forest, vowing not to utter a single word for twelve years.

At the end of that time he began to preach, and soon attracted many followers. They asked questions and, unlike his own teachers, he answered all their questions. His disciples gathered into books the teachings of Mahavira. These are called: Agamas, The Precepts. These became their Sacred Scriptures. Mahavira's followers became known as Jains and their religion is called Jainism.

There are about two million followers of Jainism in India today. Their religion has become quite complicated by the many explanations and the teachings that have been added to the Agamas during twenty-five centuries.

The young Prince Vardhamana who was renamed in his youth Mahavira, is now known as The Lord Mahavira, and he is best remembered by the world for his First Commandment. It consists of one word:

Ahimsa.

It means, "non-injury." And it teaches that it is forbidden to his followers to injure any living thing, for every creature has a soul. And it is better to die in the attempt to be kind and helpful, than to live at the cost of pain to others. It is better to behave like the pigeon than the fowler.

When they who believe in him think of Mahavira, they think of *Ahimsa.*

IV. ZARATHUSTRA: The Golden Star

Beautiful Dhugova

Some three or five or seven thousand years ago (the scholars are not agreed upon the date), there lived a maiden in a distant province of the land of Iran, or Aryan, or Ariyana, as it is called in their Sacred Books; and her name was Dhugova. The maiden Dhugova was supremely beautiful. When she appeared in the darkest of rooms, it at once became illuminated from the brightness of her face; and her presence gave warmth to the coldest place.

Such unnatural beauty frightened Durasan, the Chief Magician of Iran, and he feared that nothing good would ever come from Dhugova. He ordered a watch about the home of her parents, lest Dhugova might do something to displease the gods; and he secretly instructed his officers to seek an opportunity to kill her. The plot became known to the girl's father, and he sent her away to the town of Rae, in the province of Azerbaijan, west of the Caspian Sea.

There Dhugova remained, and there she met a young man named Porushasp Spitama. From his name we gather that he might have had something to do with horses, for his name means: "He of the Spitama clan who keeps many horses."

Even three, even five, even seven thousand years ago boys and girls fell in love. And Porushasp Spitama fell in love with the beautiful Dhugova. They were married in a great house on the banks of the river Darejia, within view of Mount Jabar, in a wedding far from ordinary. For Porushasp was a descendant of the great Persian King Minocheher. And his uncles and his nephews, and his cousins once removed, twice removed, thrice removed, and all his other relatives, were Spitamans who never failed to gather at the wedding or funeral of a kinsman.

The Magician's Defeat

A year and a day after her marriage, Dhugova gave birth to a son. And when the midwife spanked the newly born infant, instead of crying, he burst into laughter. His mother laughed with him, and named him Zarathustra, which means: Golden Star.

Pliny the Elder, the Roman author of the First Century, wrote in his celebrated Natural History *that "Zoroaster [the Latin name for Zarathustra] was the only human being who ever laughed on the same day on which he was born."*

When Durasan learned of Zarathustra's birth, and his laughter on the day he was born, the Chief Magician of

Iran was certain it boded no good. He called together his trusted seers before the king and said to them:

"We must destroy this child before he grows up to destroy us!"

"Yes," agreed the king, "and you are the one who must carry this out." For he would not trust anyone else to do it.

Durasan traveled in disguise to the home of the child. He stole into the infant's room when it was left unattended, pulled out his sharp dagger, and quickly lifted his arm to stab the child. He lifted his arm, but he did not lower it. For Durasan's arm had ossified, and he could not move the solid bone.

"The Fire God is angry," thought Durasan. "He wants to consume this child."

The Chief Magician returned home and ordered a great fire built on the altar of his temple. Then he sent word to Porushasp to bring his son to the gods.

The father obeyed and Durasan placed the child on the burning pyre built for the Fire God.

Dhugova hurried to the Fire Temple. And there she found Zarathustra playing in the flames as if they were the gentle cooling waves of summer waters, laughing as he had laughed on the day of his birth. Dhugova snatched her child from the altar and carried him home.

"The God of Kine is angry," thought Durasan, "for he wants to trample the child to death."

The Chief Magician sent word to Porushasp to bring Zarathustra to worship the God of the Kine. Then Durasan placed the child on a very narrow road and had a herd of cattle stampeded in that direction.

Dhugova, who had come in anxiety to watch over her child, saw the first cow to reach the boy step over him carefully, then remain fixed in the path to protect him from harm. The cow firmly held her place until the entire herd had passed. Then she moved on. Dhugova rushed over and picked up her laughing son.

"The God of the Wolves is angry," thought Durasan, "for he wants to devour this child."

And the Chief Magician ordered the child to be placed in a den of wolves, and to be left there for two days.

"If the wolves do not devour him," thought Durasan, "Zarathustra will die of hunger within two days."

The child was placed in a den in the jungle and abandoned. When the wolves arrived they could smell the sweet flesh of the child in their lair. They bared their teeth, ready to pounce upon their prey and tear him to pieces. But as they opened their mouths, their jaws became locked; and when they tried to move forward, their feet became riveted to the ground. The terrified wolves turned in panic and fled.

Dhugova, who had hurried to the den of the wolves at the end of the time set by the Chief Magician, found her son lying contentedly on the ground while two mountain goats were feeding him as if he were one of their own young. The happy mother lifted her child up in her arms, and again he laughed as he had on the day he was born.

Still Durasan would not give up his evil plotting against the infant.

In every folklore of the world, the birth and early youth of a great prophet is clothed in the miraculous. First come the miracles at birth; and then the great dangers overcome in the marvelous escapes from the evil plottings of those fearing the coming of the prophet. Then follow the miracles performed by the boy prophet in early youth. The lore of Zarathustra's life follows in this traditional folklore pattern.

The Ball of Fire

When Zarathustra reached the age of seven, his mother said to his father:

"Our son is destined for greatness. We must give him a good education."

"You are right," the father agreed. "I shall send him to the great teacher, Burzin-kurus. From him our son will learn all that there is to learn in religion, farming, medicine, and the arts of living."

Zarathustra spent the next eight years with the great teacher. He astonished Burzin-kurus with his ability to absorb knowledge. The teacher would give him the first word, and the pupil would recite the rest of the sentence; the teacher would explain the first principle, and the pupil would interpret all its meanings.

But outside of his keenness of mind, Zarathustra seemed like all the other students during the years at school. Except for one thing:

The ball of fire in his hand.

From the day he arrived at school, he carried a small ball of fire in the palm of his hand. It never burned his hand and it never left his hand.

This sign from heaven of his prophetic future, Zarathustra had with him always.

It was with him during the eight years at school, and he carried it with him when he left school, at the age of fifteen, and entered the army to heal the wounded during the bitter war his people fought at that time with the Turanians.

He carried the ball of fire with him when he married the lovely Havovee, and during the following ten years when he wandered over the land, helping the poor and the needy as a teacher and healer.

The ball of fire was with him when he retired to Mount Sabalan for months of solitude, trying to understand the meaning of life and the source of good and evil in the world.

And it was still with him on that wonderful day when Zarathustra, watching a sunset, suddenly received in a flash of revelation, the key to the understanding he was seeking:

There was day and there was night;

There was light and there was darkness;

There was truth and there was falsehood.

The whole of life consisted of two great forces in constant conflict with each other.

The name of one force was *Ahura Mazda* — the Power of Good; the name of the other was *Angra Manyu* — the Power of Evil.

The sign of the ball of fire had been fulfilled. Now Zarathustra saw clearly the nature of the world, and how man ought to live to help *Ahura Mazda* conquer *Angra Manyu.*

The Zend-Avesta (Zoroastrianism)

In the course of many centuries, the teachings of Zarathustra (who is best known in the Western world as Zoroaster) were gathered into books, known as the Avestas. These are a collection similar to our own Bible, though not as large nor as varied.

The first part of the Avestas is a collection of hymns, like our Psalms, and called Gathas. Many scholars believe that these might have been written down originally by Zoroaster himself.

The second part of the Avestas contains a narrative of Creation and the Laws of Ahura Mazda to guide the good Zoroastrian. It is called Vendidad, and might be likened to the Genesis and Leviticus of our Bible.

To these have been added a number of other books. And later, to the Zoroastrian Sacred Books were added interpretations of the earlier books. These are called Zend, and the entire work is called Zend-Avesta.

When Alexander the Great conquered Persia, in the fourth century before the Christian Era, he tried to convert the people to the Greek religion. He therefore ordered all the Zoroastrian Sacred Books burned. And it is believed that he took one copy back to Greece where it was translated into Greek. But only fragments of the old Avestas escaped destruction.

Some five centuries later an attempt was made to gather all fragments and reconstruct the Zoroastrian Sacred Books. The task was scarcely completed, when the Arabs conquered Persia in the seventh century of our era, and again the Zoroastrian books were destroyed, and the Persians forced to abandon their religion at the point of the sword.

A number of Zoroastrians escaped to India, where they were permitted to practice their religion. They were called by the Hindus, Parsis or Persians. And that is their name in India to this day.

There are only about 100,000 Parsis in India, followers of the teachings of Zarathustra, the Golden Star. But the smallness of their numbers is no gauge of the greatness of their religion. For in spite of the fact that so few, today, are Zoroastrians, many in other religions recognize in this — perhaps the oldest of the living religions — an inspiring system of belief among the various attempts made by man to explain the meaning of life; and how man ought to behave toward God in Heaven and toward Man on Earth.

V. CONFUCIUS:
K'ung the Philosopher

Encounter with a Unicorn

In the mountainous Kingdom of Lu, not far from the Kwang-ho River, there lived a man named Shuh-liang-Heih, whose family name was K'ung. Shuh was as tall as an oak and as strong as a buffalo. And throughout the Kingdom of Lu he was known for fearlessness in the face of danger, and called Shuh the Valiant.

Because of his valor, and because of his royal descent, Shuh-Liang-Heih was appointed head of the District of Tsow, near the Yellow Sea. Here he was greatly admired, for he ruled his district with justice and devotion. And equally admired was his beautiful wife Ching-Tsai, noted for her five constant virtues: benevolence, righteousness, propriety, wisdom, and sincerity.

The K'ungs had everything to make them happy — that is, everything except a son. Nine children were born to them, but not a single son to worship at their shrine after they were gone.

And so the years went by.

One day Ching-Tsai walked along a path under the cinnamon trees in the garden, absorbed in thought. Suddenly an animal jumped out of the juniper bushes and stopped right in front of her. It had the body of a colt, but from the middle of its forehead grew a long tapered horn.

Ching-Tsai knew at once that it was a unicorn. She had known about the unicorn from childhood as one of the Five Rulers of the Earth, the Symbol of Felicity, the Emblem of Longevity, and the Omen of Beneficence. And there it stood before her, near enough to be touched.

Ching-Tsai took a silken ribbon and placed it gently upon the tip of the unicorn's horn. But when she put her hand out toward its body, the unicorn turned and sped into the juniper bushes whence it had come. Ching-Tsai remained there for a long time looking in the direction in which it had disappeared. Then her gaze wandered to the ground and she noticed at her feet a tiny jade tablet. She picked it up and saw upon the jade the inscription:

> *You shall have a son who will bring felicity and beneficence to the world. He will become a king without a kingdom.*

Ching-Tsai told nothing of her encounter to her husband, who was now seventy years old. She wondered whether her meeting with the unicorn was a vision. But she could not explain the jade tablet that she now wore as an amulet about her neck.

Nine months later, in the Second Moon of the Twenty-fourth year of the reign of Ling Wang, Ching-Tsai looked out of the window one day and saw two winged dragons, rulers of the east and of spring, guarding the entrance to the house. But she thought less of them and more of the pain and mystery of birth. For at that very moment Ching-Tsai gave birth to her tenth child — a son.

The happiness of the aging Shuh the Valiant could be seen upon his face. He decorated his garden with many lanterns, and called out joyfully to everyone who passed:

"I have a son now!"

"Kung-hi!" they congratulated him formally. "What are you going to call him?"

"I shall call him Ch'iu — Ch'iu K'ung."

"May he be as valiant as his father!" they responded.

The Sight of a Comet

From his earliest childhood, Ch'iu heard many stories, for the Chinese have always been great creators and tellers of legends. Long before his education began, his parents introduced him to the story of Creation, from the time when there was nothing, to the time there was the First Man, *P'an Ku*, who set the sun and the moon in the heavens, then called the Unicorn, the Dragon, the Phoenix, the Tortoise, and the White Tiger to help him rule the earth and all that was in it.

His mother loved to tell him the stories of the Immortals. She told him about the Immortal Chung-Li-Ch'uan, who went about China with a peach in his left hand and a fan in his right, reviving the dead. And she told him about the Immortal Chang-Kuo-Lao, who rode about the land on a white donkey. When he stopped, he would magically reduce his donkey to the size of a small piece of paper and place it in his wallet. Then he would go about performing great feats of magic. When Chang-Kuo-Lao decided to move on to another part of the country, he would make the donkey reappear by pouring water on his wallet, and then he would ride away.

These and many similar stories young Ch'iu was told.

But strangely enough, he did not like them. From the very beginning the child Ch'iu found all talk of the supernatural distasteful and unpleasant.

And just as he was repelled by the supernatural, he was fascinated by the laws of nature and the natural. He asked a million questions about the customs and the rituals of his people, and about the world of reality about him.

It is told about him that when he was still a very small child he studied his elders when they bowed, since bowing is part of the ceremony of worship. He began to bow to the ancestral tablets in his father's house, set in the shadows and always fragrant with incense. He bowed to his father and his mother each time they went away from home for a visit. He bowed to the friends of his parents when he saw them in the street, or when they came to visit the family. When alone in the garden, he bowed to the rosebushes and thanked them for their fragrance; he bowed to the stone benches, and thanked them for their hardness and smoothness; and he bowed to the sky, because he found it so beautiful.

His father died when Ch'iu was only a few years old, and the boy bowed at the tomb as prescribed by custom. And when poverty overtook the family after Shuh the Valiant died, Ch'iu bowed to poverty without complaining.

Bowing was part of being polite; and Ch'iu enjoyed politeness as one enjoys good music. He considered politeness a prime virtue.

As soon as his education began, Ch'iu started to delve into the Li Chi, the Book of Rites, the Chinese classic concerned with rites and ceremonies and with everything customary and orderly. He went on to the Shi Ching, the Book of Odes, and other great classics. By the time he was fifteen, young Ch'iu had already won a great reputation as an authority on all the classics, known as The Five Classics.

The more Ch'iu studied the laws of nature and the books of ceremony and ritual, the greater became his dislike for all talk of miracles, ghosts and spirits, and every variety of the supernatural.

One dark night, so the story is told, Ch'iu walked alone along the street. Suddenly a comet appeared moving across the dark sky with a long and luminous tail. Instead of being fascinated by the unusual spectacle, Ch'iu went home sick at heart at the sight of something counter to the order of the skies as he knew it. And for three days he remained in bed, upset by the appearance of something that disturbed the heavenly order where everything moves according to a divine plan.

When he was well again, he began to think that perhaps comets are part of the divine plan, and he ascended to a high place to bow to the heavenly guest. But by that time there was no sign of the comet.

The Lute at Daybreak

In Ch'iu's time it was proper for young men to marry at eighteen. And when Ch'iu K'ung was eighteen, he sat down and wrote in eight Chinese characters the year, the month, the day, and the hour when a certain maiden, named Ki K'iu, was born. This note he sent to her father, which was the proper way to make known that he wanted to marry her.

Ki's father, when he received the note, called his daughter to his side, and said:

"My child, you have reached the age when a girl should marry. And Ch'iu K'ung, son of Shuh the Valiant, has sent your birth date to me. Ch'iu is already famed for his knowledge of the Five Classics and for his great wisdom. He has many students and they call him K'ung-fu-tzu (Confucius), which means K'ung the Philosopher. To be sure, he is poor. But he has an emperor among his ancestors, and though he is not yet eighteen, he has already been appointed Manager of the Granaries by the King of Lu. But you must know that Confucius is a great believer in ancient rites. If you marry him, you will have to observe the three hundred ceremonial forms and the three thousand rules of decorum. What do you say, my daughter?"

"If I marry him, will I be able to play my lute at daybreak?" asked Ki.

"You will," said the father.

And so it was settled. Confucius sent his bride-to-be lilies and heliotrope, melons and pomegranates, as prescribed by custom. And on the day proper for them to be married, they were married in the most proper way.

The young bride tried to memorize the names of all the sacred books her husband taught to his many pupils; and she approved smilingly of everything he asked her to do. But without asking his consent, she awoke each morning before dawn and when everybody was still asleep she softly played her lute in the garden.

At first Confucius thought it was strange that his bride should wake to play when others were asleep; and also her music disturbed him, for it spoke of things he had not known existed. He bought new lutes for her, hoping that on the new instruments she would play other tunes. But Ki could play only at daybreak and only on the old lute that she had used since childhood in her father's garden.

One day Confucius found himself singing. And he discovered that he was singing the tunes his girl-wife had played in the garden at sunrise. The young philosopher then added music to his studies and soon became an accomplished player himself. When his wife complained that she was ignorant and could not add to his knowledge of sacred texts or records of the ancient emperors, he would reply:

"You have given me more than books or teachers could have given me. You have given me a love for music, which I learned by listening to you play your lute at daybreak."

Confucius Said –

Like a folk song which goes out among the people and is repeated from mouth to ear and from ear to mouth, the fame of Confucius traveled throughout the country. His words were repeated in the north and the south, in the east and the west. Young and old, ignorant and learned, gained understanding by his teachings. And he taught in language everyone could understand. He never talked in riddles. He never discussed death or the world of the spirits or what goes on in heaven. He taught only how people ought to live and how they ought to seek and gain happiness through the right behavior.

Often his teachings would be presented in the form of a proverb, easy to grasp and easy to remember.

Before long the Sayings of Confucius became the heritage of every citizen of Cathay. Students streamed in from all the provinces in the land. And at one time, it is claimed, he had as many as three thousand students and followers gathered around him.

He taught the principles of courage and prudence.

He taught the value of education and of self-criticism.

He taught the principles of filial duty.

He taught the principles of selecting friends.

He taught the principles of good human relations.

He taught the principles of good government.

And above all he taught his students how to appreciate the arts in everyday living.

"He who does not study poetry," he said, "is like a man whose face is ever turned toward the wall."

On another occasion he said: "A man without charity of heart, what has he to do with music?"

Confucius extolled the virtue of knowing right from wrong; and he insisted that knowing what is wrong and not trying to right it, that is the greatest wrong.

The teachings of Confucius conquered the kingdoms of China more thoroughly than if they had been subdued by arms. Though he was not a religious leader, and disclaimed the discovery of new wisdom, he became the nation's beloved Teacher, not only in his own time, but in all the generations following.

The teachings and sayings of Confucius have been collected in the Four Books. The most important of these is the first, The Analects of Confucius, which contain a compilation of his proverbs and of conversations between Confucius and his disciples.

The Analects is in no sense a religious book. It is a collection of moral ideas, a sheaf of golden rules, that the people of China found as worthy as any of their sacred books.

And it is because of his Sayings that, in the hearts of four hundred million people, Confucius takes his place beside the Buddha and Lao-tzu.

Death of a Unicorn

When Confucius was seventy-two years old, according to legend, a hunter came to him and said:

"O Master! A strange thing has befallen me today and I want you to tell me what it means."

"Go on, my son," said Confucius.

"I was hunting in the forest all day and toward evening I shot what I thought was a deer. But when I came near the animal, I found that it was not a deer at all. And I brought it with me for you to see."

The huntsman dragged his prey in before Confucius. The old teacher bent over and he saw a creature with the body of a colt, and a single tapering horn growing out of the center of its forehead.

"This is a unicorn," said Confucius deeply stirred. "You have killed a unicorn, my son."

The sage looked again at the unicorn and saw that upon its horn, badly faded, hung a very old silken ribbon.

"Before I was born," Confucius went on, "so my mother often told me, she saw a unicorn in my father's garden so close to her that she placed a ribbon upon its horn."

"What do you think it means?" asked the hunter.

"I do not live by signs and I abhor divination," said the old teacher.

That night Confucius could not fall asleep. He left his bed and walked out into the garden. The night was dark and chilly. Nothing stirred, and not a sound, near or far, disturbed the stillness. The trees and grass and beds of flowers were masses of soft shadows. In the dome of the sky the bright stars seemed to huddle together. He had never seen the earth covered so richly in dark purple. He could not remember a night quite so still. He had never seen, he was certain, stars quite so brilliant and set in an ocean so mysteriously deep. It was akin to music. And he suddenly felt a great desire to play upon his lute.

He went back into the house and soon returned with his instrument. By then the eastern horizon was faintly paling. Confucius began to play. And he tried to express in sound what he could not express in words — the feelings that had gathered in his heart. He played until daybreak came and daybreak passed. Then he returned to his room, put away his lute, stretched out in his bed and closed his eyes. Forever.

That was in 479 B.C., on the eighteenth day of the Fourth Moon, in the year Yen Sin.

VI. LAO-TZU: The Old Philosopher

Plum-Tree-Ears

We can gauge the greatness of a man in the eyes of his people by the legends they create about him — especially those concerning his childhood and youth. For it would seem that, in the hearts of the people, he whom they accept as a prophet in maturity they believe to be one favored of the gods from the day he is born.

In the folklore the birth, infancy, and youth of a great leader is always astonishing and miraculous. If children normally learn to walk when they are a year old, these great ones are described as having learned to walk immediately after birth; if other children normally learn how to write at the age of seven or eight, these inspired ones at the age of eight know all the scripts in the world, their differences, their peculiarities, and the symbolic meaning of each letter. While they are still infants, they perform great cures. At their touch the crooked become straight; the deaf gain their hearing; the blind, their sight; the mute, their voice; and the sick become well.

Though we often know very little, if anything, about the circumstances of the birth of the great religious leaders of long ago, the lore which grew up about them much later describes in vivid detail everything that happened in their lives. And the further back into childhood and infancy the folk tales go, the more precise are their details of the miraculous events.

The record of some of these leaders begins with their infancy, as in the case of Moses. The record of others begins with their parents, as in the case of Mohammed. Still other records begin with remoter antecedents, as in the case of Jesus. And the stories of the life of Buddha go back five hundred and fifty reincarnations. (The Birth Stories of Gautama and the five hundred and fifty lives he lived before he was born as Prince Siddhartha Gautama are given in the Jatakas.)

There is, however, one great religious leader about whom the folklore tells us practically nothing. He lived in China about 2500 years ago, the son of a very poor man in the province of Ho-nan, and he is known to the world as the Old Philosopher, Lao-tzu.

When Lao-tzu was seventy years old, he wished to leave the province of Loyang. At the border the guard insisted that the Old Philosopher must first write down his teachings before he could pass. Lao-tzu sat down and wrote out about twenty-five pages of what he called the Tao-Teh-King: The Book of Reason and Virtue. Then the guard allowed the Old Philosopher to cross the border of the province.

He was never heard of again.

The small book left behind by the Old Philosopher has become the Sacred Scriptures of a religion that now has millions of followers, called Taoists. And though the Tao-Teh-King is such a little book, thousands of heavy volumes have been written about it by the followers of Lao-tzu. The Tao-Teh-King is one of the most difficult books to understand. And Lao-tzu did not make it easy for anyone to try to explain his teachings. For he said that the one who knows what the teachings mean does not tell; and the one who tells does not know. Naturally, anyone who tried to explain the Old Philosopher was suspected of himself not understanding.

Yet not all the teachings are difficult. Some are clear and as refreshing as the waters of a mountain stream. Here are a few examples:

"The great object of the Good Man is to keep peace. He takes no pleasure in winning battles or in killing his fellow men."

"To those who are good to me I am good; and to those who are not good to me I am good. In that way all can learn to be good."

"A truly good man loves all men and hates none."

"If people are hard to govern it is because they are too wise."

Taoism found a great following and when Buddhism entered China, Taoism combined with it, and the people derived strength and guidance from both. To this day the

Chinese people, 400 million of them, believe in Confucianism, Buddhism, and Taoism at the same time.

It is strange that with such a great following, the Taoists did not create any generally accepted legends about the infancy and childhood of their religious leader.

Are there then no legends at all about the life of Lao-tzu? There is one:

There lived a poor farmer in the village of Keuh-Jin, in the mountainous Kingdom of Ch'u, whose wife, Li-Peh-Yang expected a child. She bore the child for many long years, nine times nine years, and still her child was not yet born. Meanwhile the farmer died, and his widow wandered about in search of work to earn her bread.

Then, in the third year of the Twenty-First Sovereign of the Dynasty of Chow, Li-Peh-Yang finally gave birth to a boy in a field under a plum tree.

The child was born eighty-one years old. His hair was white and his skin was wrinkled, and he had a long white beard like a man eighty-one years old.

Because he was born under a plum tree, and because his ear lobes were so long, the mother named her child Plum-Tree-Ears. But when she showed her child to the people of the countryside, they looked at his white hair and wise look in astonishment, and called him Lao-tzu — the Old Philosopher.

VII. ABRAHAM: The Boy Who Discovered God

The Birth of Abraham

In the land of the Chaldees there lived a king, long ago, whose name was Nimrod. So vain and wicked was this king that he claimed to be a god, and beheaded anyone inclined to doubt it.

One night the royal stargazers came to Nimrod and said: "We have seen a star in the skies so bright that all the other stars paled beside it. This foretells the birth of a man who will destroy our gods and take the crown from your head."

"What can we do?" asked the king. (He always said "we" when he needed protection; and he always said "I" when he issued decrees.)

"Send out a decree that the midwives must destroy all male infants at birth. Then you will assure the boy's death and save your crown."

The royal decree was sent out and seventy thousand infants were killed. But one woman, Entelai, the wife of Terah, fled from the city of Ur-Kuta to the desert and hid in a cave when the time came for her to give birth to her child.

The dark cave became lighted as if by the noonday sun

when Entelai entered, and she gave birth without pain to a boy.

She named her son Abraham; made him comfortable, and with the tears streaming from her eyes, said to her infant:

"If you are truly favored by the gods, they will care for you. But I must leave at once or the king's men will search for me until they find me. Then both of us will perish."

And Entelai abandoned her child.

Nimrod and Terah

The king's soothsayers discovered by divination that a son had been born to Terah the Idolmaker and his wife, Entelai. And that Terah's son was the child the king was seeking.

King Nimrod summoned Terah before him and said:

"The seers have learned of the birth of your son who is destined to cause us and our gods much evil. I will give you his weight in gold and silver if you will bring him to me that I may destroy him."

"Your majesty," said Terah the Idolmaker, "you remind me of the man who said to the horse, 'I will give you your weight in rye and wheat, if you will let me cut off your head first.' And the horse said, 'Who will eat the rye and wheat if my head is cut off?' If you kill my son, who will inherit the gold and silver you offer me?"

"I shall have you beheaded, if you fail to bring me your first-born son within three days," said the wicked king in a rage.

Terah returned home and found that one of his servants had given birth to a stillborn child. This child he brought to the king and said:

"When I came home, I found my wife in grief and my first-born child dead. Here he is for you to do with him as you wish."

Abraham Makes a Discovery

When Entelai left the cave, an angel came and placed a stone in Abraham's right hand, and then he placed a stone in the infant's left hand. From the first stone flowed milk, and from the second stone flowed honey.

From time to time, the mother would secretly visit her baby, and her heart was delighted to see him thrive.

One day, when Abraham was still very young, he walked out of the cave and saw the bright sun for the first time. He looked about him and thought: "The sun must be the ruler and creator of this beautiful world!"

And he worshiped the sun.

But that evening, when he came out of the cave, he saw that the sun was gone; and the moon and the stars had replaced the sun in the heavens. "The moon and the stars," thought Abraham, "must be the rulers of the world!"

And he worshiped them.

But the next morning the sun was out again, and there was no sign of the moon and the stars in the skies.

"The ruler of the world," thought Abraham, "must be He who created the sun, the moon and the stars, and the earth with everything in it. It is He who keeps them all in motion."

And when his mother came to visit him the next time Abraham said to her:

"I do not fear King Nimrod any longer. For I have found One who rules over Nimrod."

"Is there a god even greater than our king?" asked the astonished mother.

"There is One who is the God of Gods and the Ruler of Rulers. He is the One God who created heaven and earth."

Then Abraham returned to Ur-Kuta with his mother.

The Breaking of the Idols

At home, Abraham helped his father, who made clay idols. Terah made idols to protect people against sickness, to keep away evil spirits, to bring good luck in marriage, to make crops prosper, to protect households against thieves, and various other kinds of idols.

One day, when Abraham was alone in his father's shop, a woman came in to buy an idol that would protect her home from thieves.

"Don't you have one now?" asked Abraham in surprise.

"We had one," the woman explained, "but he was stolen."

"How can you expect an idol to protect your family against thieves when it cannot protect itself against thieves?"

"But we must believe in *something!*" the woman insisted.

"How old are you?" asked Abraham.

"I am sixty years old," the woman replied.

"There is not an idol in my father's shop that is more than a week old. And if you want to know what strength these idols have, just watch me — "

Abraham took an ax and started to smash the idols. The woman ran out of the store, but Abraham went on smashing the idols until only one remained. He placed the ax in the arms of the remaining idol, then sat down and waited for his father.

When Terah returned, he demanded: "Abraham, what have you done?"

"I have done nothing," said Abraham innocently. "A woman came and offered sacrifices to one of the idols. Whereupon this one took the ax and destroyed all the others."

"Abraham, how can you say such things? You know that these clay images cannot move or fight!"

"Then why do you make them, and why do people worship them?"

And old Terah did not know how to answer him.

Trial by Fire

Meanwhile word reached King Nimrod that Abraham, son of Terah, had smashed the idols in his father's shop. He summoned Abraham and demanded:

"Why did you destroy the gods sacred to our people?"

"Because there is no power or spirit in them," answered Abraham.

"Then worship fire," said the king.

"Water can extinguish fire," said Abraham.

"Then worship water," said the king.

"The clouds can carry the water away," said Abraham.

"Then worship the clouds."

"Wind can disperse the clouds," said Abraham.

"Then worship the wind," said Nimrod.

"I would rather worship the One God in heaven, who created all things, including the wind."

King Nimrod ordered his men to throw Abraham into a great furnace to destroy him by fire. But at the end of the three days, when the gates to the furnace were opened, Abraham was seen walking around in the flames unscathed, as if he were promenading in a pleasant garden.

Nimrod's heart began to pound, his hands began to shake, and his voice began to quaver:

"Leave your father's house and my land," he begged, "and I shall give you gold and silver, and whatever gifts you may desire. But leave!"

And Abraham left his father's house, and his kinsmen, and his native land, to preach against idols wherever he went.

The Many Adventures

We are told that Abraham lived to the age of one hundred seventy-five years, and all his days were full of wondrous events.

He traveled far and through many dangers.

He witnessed the destruction of the wicked twin cities, Sodom and Gomorrah.

To rescue his nephew Lot he, and a handful of men, waged war against five mighty kings and their hosts.

He became the father of two nations: from his son by his wife Hagar, came the nation of the Ishmaelites; and from his son by his wife Sarah, came the nation of the Israelites.

So faithful was he to God that when asked to sacrifice his best-beloved son, Abraham unwaveringly placed him on the altar to carry out God's command.

These, and many other deeds are claimed for Abraham.

Yet it is not because of any of these that Abraham is remembered.

All the stories about Abraham were born long, long after he died. For we really know nothing for certain about Abraham, son of Terah, from Ur-Kuta in the Chaldees. All we know is that he was the first man on earth to have come to the belief in One God through his own reasoning and his own observations.

And it is for this great concept that Abraham is remembered and honored.

VIII. MOSES: The Lawgiver

Pharaoh's Decree

There lived an old wizard in Egypt, over thirty-five hundred years ago, whose name was Plti — and you can pronounce his name any way you please as long as it sounds like Plti. This wizard was versed in the knowledge of the Books of Signs, forecasts by the stars, divination by oracles, predictions by the winds, omens in the smoke of sacrifices, and he could also use magic and charms on every occasion.

One day the old wizard said to the Pharaoh: "For four hundred years the Hebrews have been faithful slaves in Egypt. But now I foresee trouble."

"What kind of trouble?" asked the suspicious king.

The old wizard pointed to the royal physician and said: "That kind of trouble."

"But that is my beloved physician," the king protested.

"He is Amram and a Hebrew. And within forty days his wife will conceive a son who will free the Hebrews from their slavery and cause the downfall of Egypt. Unless — "

"Unless — what?" asked the worried king.

"Unless the child does not grow up," said the wizard with a grin.

Pharaoh was weak but not wicked. He did not like the idea of killing infants.

"How do I know that you divine properly and foretell correctly?" asked the king sternly.

"I have consulted the stars," said Plti. "I have poured molten wax. I have examined the entrails of a fish. I have observed a royal cock picking up grain on the temple grounds. I have drawn pebbles from a heap. I have looked into the mirrors at midnight. And I have peered down into the reflections of the fountains. Each time the prediction was the same. I give you this as a sign of the truth of my forecast: before the day is over you shall dream a dream that will confirm the truth of what I have foretold."

That afternoon Pharaoh fell asleep and he dreamt that a young man came riding toward him on the back of a lion, holding on to the mane with his left hand, and with the right striking the king's head. Then the rider on the lion caught the king by his leg, swung him around over his head, and flung him into the sea.

Pharaoh awoke, trembling with fear. He immediately called together his stargazers to tell them his dream.

"Your dream," said Plti, "means just what I told you this morning. We are in danger from an infant yet unborn. Unless — "

"Unless we destroy the child at birth," the king completed. "But how shall we know which is the one we fear?"

"That is simple," said Plti. "Destroy them all."

"Is there no other way but by slaughter?" asked Pharaoh.

"Order all the Hebrews to be separated from their wives for forty days," said Plti. "And place Amram in prison for exactly forty days. In that way the child will not even be conceived. And just to make certain, order all midwives to kill at birth every male child born to the Hebrews ten months from now and also on the eleventh month and the twelfth, just to make sure."

The decree was issued to all Egyptian midwives.

But on the eleventh month, the stargazers came to the Pharaoh and said: "We see that a male child was born last night in the house of Amram the Levite, and the midwives did not destroy him. For he was born to his mother without pain and she did not consult the midwives."

Pharaoh dispatched his chief officer to Amram's house with the order to destroy the child by fire. When the officer, Haman, entered the house, he found that the mother had placed the infant in the brick oven, where a great fire seemed to be burning.

The mother explained to the king's emissary: "I learned of the king's wish to destroy my child, and I placed him in the oven."

When Haman left the house to report to the king, the mother lifted her child out of the oven, where the infant's bright face had shone like the bright flames of a fire.

For three months the mother, Jocheved, succeeded in hiding her son from the neighbors. Then she realized that she could hide him no longer and she asked her husband to prepare a waterproof basket, lined with down. Jocheved placed her little son in the basket, and let it float down the Nile.

Princess Thermutis

The baby's sister, Miriam, went down to the Nile and hid herself among the bushes to see what became of her infant brother cast adrift in the basket. Soon she saw Pharaoh's daughter, the Princess Thermutis, and her handmaidens come down to bathe in the river. The princess suffered from a disfiguring skin disease that distressed her in hot weather. The day was unbearably hot, and the princess hurried into the water to cool off. As she and her attendants were diverting themselves in the water, they suddenly heard the cry of an infant.

Miriam heard the princess say:

"Go, fetch the child to me."

"O mistress, this must be one of the Hebrew children that your father, the king, ordered drowned," the servant replied. "I fear to transgress your father's command!"

"Then I shall get him myself," said Thermutis.

She went out among the bulrushes where the basket rested, and pulled it toward her. Her servants shouted in surprise. For the moment the princess touched the basket, the disfiguring disease vanished from her skin. And the maidens were astonished at her beauty.

"He has cured me of my illness," said Thermutis, "and I shall adopt him as my son."

All the maidens surrounded their mistress to admire the beauty of the foundling. And after the princess had sworn them all to secrecy, they returned to the palace with the child.

The next day Miriam came again to the river's edge and she heard the princess telling in distress that her foundling had refused the milk of all the nurses she could find; and if he refused to eat, he would surely die.

Miriam came forward and said: "O Princess, perhaps if you called a Hebrew nurse he might accept her milk."

"Find me such a nurse," said Thermutis, "and bring her to me."

Miriam ran home for her mother, Jocheved. And the child was placed with his mother until the weaning. For two years Jocheved took care of her child, under the king's protection.

Amram had named his son "Heber" because that means, in Hebrew, "we were reunited." Jocheved called him "Jekuthiel," meaning "God gave him back to me." His sister Miriam called him "Jered," which means "descended," because her brother was saved when she descended to watch him in the stream.

But Princess Thermutis called her adopted son, whom

she had saved from drowning, by the name that he carried all his life: Moses. For in Egyptian, *Mo* means "water" and *Uses* means "one saved from drowning."

How Moses Acquired a Lisp

Moses was reared in the palace, and everyone there came to love the child. Even Pharaoh treated him as if he were a grandson. Until one day, as Pharaoh was playing with the child on his knee, Moses climbed up, took off the king's glittering crown and placed it on his own small head.

The wise men in the palace looked on with consternation. And the wizard Plti at once advised:

"Chop off the child's head, for he has committed an offense punishable by death!"

"It is an offense punishable by death only if the child knew what he did and did it on purpose," said another wizard.

"How can we find out whether or not he did it on purpose?" asked the king.

One of the court advisers (the Angel Gabriel under this guise), replied:

"If it please the king, place before the child two platters, one bearing a precious gem and the other, a live coal. If the child reaches for the gem, you will know that he took your crown from choice and deserves to be slain. But if he reaches for the coal, you will know that he did not do this deed deliberately."

This counsel pleased the king and two platters were placed before the child, one platter bearing a gem and the other, a coal. Moses at once stretched out his hand toward the gleaming gem. But the angel pushed away his hand and the child grabbed the hot coal. Moses quickly stuck his scorched fingers into his mouth, and as he did so the child burned his lips and tongue. For the rest of his days this affected his speech, and Moses lisped.

Moses the Warrior

While Moses grew up in the palace of the king and was raised as an Egyptian prince, the Ethiopians declared war on Egypt. They invaded small part by small part, intimidating the people. The farther the Egyptians were willing to retreat before the victors, the farther the Ethiopians went in their demands. Until, in the end, they began to dream of conquering the whole of Egypt and making its population a subject people.

Moses was still very young at the time, but he went to Pharaoh and offered to lead the Egyptians against the enemy. His offer pleased everybody. Those in the court who loved and trusted him rejoiced in his eagerness to save the nation, and they prayed for his success. And those in the court who envied his position, hoped that he would be killed in battle, and they prayed for his downfall.

Moses assembled his army and studied the plans of the

enemy. He learned that they expected him to meet them in battle along a certain river bank. Moses stationed men along the river to lead the enemy to believe that he would fight as they expected. But he secretly moved his main army by land to the rear of the enemy's lines and laid siege to their cities, far in their rear. Whichever way the Ethiopians now turned, they were faced with disaster. The Ethiopians soon petitioned for peace and agreed to withdraw to their own borders, never again to cross into Egypt.

The victory young Moses gained over the enemy became known throughout Egypt, and his name was upon the lips of all the people. The powerful men at court who before had envied Thermutis's adopted son, now conceived an even greater hatred for him, and began to plot his destruction.

They went to the king and whispered into his ear that young Moses, now that he was victorious in battle and a favorite of the people, would not be content until he had wrested the crown from the king. They hinted that they had good reasons for their suspicions.

The king was slow to accept the slander. But his ministers and soothsayers kept dinning into his ear that he should beware of Moses.

The Day of Rest

One day, after the war with the Ethiopians, young Moses went down to the province of Goshen, where Pharaoh was building the twin cities of Pithom and Raamses with slave labor. There he saw for the first time the cruel fate that had befallen the Children of Israel.

He remained in Goshen for some time, living among the laborers, and trying to learn how he could help lighten the burden of the enslaved.

"If only we could get some rest," said the slaves. "If only we could have a day free from labor. But working, day after day and week after week and month after month, without a break, that is our greatest burden."

Moses returned to Memphis, the capital, and went directly before Pharaoh.

"O my lord and benefactor, I have a request to make of you, and I pray that you will not deny me," said Moses.

"Speak, Moses, the beloved of my household!"

"I have just returned from Goshen where I observed your Hebrew slaves. And I found them not working as well as they should."

"Let us punish them," said Pharaoh.

"O no, my lord! They do not work well because they are worn out. And they are worn out because they work without a rest. Grant them a day of rest each week, and they will become better workmen. It will profit our kingdom and will be a kindness to the laborers."

"Wisely spoken," said Pharaoh. "I will issue an edict and have it published in Goshen and in the whole of Egypt, granting your request."

And this is the edict that Pharaoh sent out:

To the Sons of Israel in Egypt, Greetings!

From this day forward you shall labor six days, but on the seventh, on Saturday, you shall rest. Thus you shall do at all times according to the command of the king and of Moses, the son of Thermutis.

In that way Moses instituted a day of rest long before a day of rest was known anywhere else in the world — even long before he brought to his people the Ten Commandments.

Trial for Murder

Moses returned to Goshen time and again. He instituted the Day of Rest, and he tried to be helpful to his people in whatever way he could. And while he was there, he saw an Egyptian overseer one day cruelly beating a young Hebrew slave.

Moses asked: "Why are you beating this man?"

"He is lazy and neglects his work," said the Egyptian. "This very hour he is supposed to be far away at his work, but instead he is here near his home."

"Why is he beating you?" asked Moses of the slave.

"I have a good wife who is also very beautiful. And every time I leave home this man, my overseer, comes to force his attentions on her. She complained to me, and today I returned to defend her. When I found him here and threatened to tell his superior he began to beat me."

"If this man tells the truth," said Moses to the Egyptian, "may God in heaven strike you dead!"

The words had scarcely left his lips when the Egyptian crumpled like a dry leaf fallen into flames, and he fell down, dead.

This was the chance the enemies of Moses had been waiting for ever since his return from the war with the Ethiopians. They accused Moses of murder; and not all the pleas of his foster mother, Thermutis, could save him from the verdict of death.

On the appointed day, the entire court assembled to witness the execution; and the enemies of the prince arrived in festive attire as if they had come to a coronation or great holiday. There was a fanfare of trumpets; Moses was brought out and led to the block, his neck bared and his hands tied behind him. Then his head was placed upon the block. A deathly stillness fell upon the arena as the executioner lifted his heavy, gleaming ax.

The ax descended with great force — and a cry of astonishment rose from all the assembled. For they saw the ax stop just before it could touch Moses' neck. The judge opened his mouth to command the executioner to try again, but the words would not leave his mouth.

Moses lifted his head from the block and started to walk away. A command was given to the guards to detain him. But the guards had become deaf at that moment and they did not hear the command. And when those who had plotted against Moses rushed forward to stop him, they became blind, and fell over each other.

Moses kept walking. He walked until he was out of the arena. He walked until he was out of Memphis; until he was beyond the borders of Egypt. And he did not stop walking until he reached Midian. There he finally sat down to rest at a shepherd's well.

The Rod of Moses

As Moses sat at the well, shepherds arrived to water their flocks. And later a young girl came near with her father's sheep. But the rude shepherds derided the girl and tried to drive her away. Moses upbraided them and watered the flock for her.

The grateful shepherdess left, and she soon returned bearing a message from her father, Jethro, inviting the stranger to come and break bread with them, and to stay with them for a while.

Soon afterwards Moses asked Jethro to give him his daughter in marriage.

"I have seven daughters," said Jethro. "Which one do you mean?"

"The one I met at the well, and whom I call 'Morning Star,' " answered Moses.

"We are Midianites," said the father. "We do not give

our daughters in marriage unless we are certain that the marriage has been deeded before birth."

"What are your signs?" asked Moses.

Without speaking a word, Jethro led the young man into his garden and pointed to a rod planted among the shrubs. It looked like an ordinary rod, such as used by shepherds. And Jethro said:

"There is a story to that rod. When I was adviser to Pharaoh in Egypt, many years ago, I saw this rod in the royal treasury, and I was told that it belonged to Joseph, son of Jacob, who saved Egypt from starvation over four hundred years ago. I asked the king to give me this rod as a gift, and he did. Later, when the king wanted me to advise him how to exterminate the Children of Israel, I ran away to Midian rather than take part in such a wicked thing. And I brought the rod with me. One day I stuck the rod into the ground where you see it now, but no matter how I tried, I could not pull it out again. Since then all the strong young men of Midian have tried to pull it out and none succeeded."

Moses bent over and looked carefully at the head of the rod and the Hebrew inscription upon it.

"There is still another story to that rod," said Moses in his lisping speech.

"What other story?" asked Jethro, puzzled.

"The Ten Wonders of the World were created by God at the end of the week of Creation. This rod was one of them. It was given to Adam when he left the Garden of Eden. Adam gave it to his son, Enoch; Enoch gave it to Shem; Shem gave it to Abraham; Abraham gave it to Isaac; Isaac gave it to Jacob; and Jacob gave it to his favorite son, Joseph. Those letters you see on the top are the letters of the Ineffable Name of God."

"And what are those letters beneath them?" asked Jethro.

"Those are the words: *Detzach-Adash-Vehachab*. These are the symbols of Ten Plagues that will befall the oppressors of the weak. For it has been decreed in heaven that he for whom this rod was meant will emancipate the Children of Israel from their slavery in Egypt."

"How can you prove that your words are true?" asked Jethro.

Moses put his hand upon the head of the rod and said: "This is my rod and was deeded for me, just as your daughter, Zipporah, was deeded to be my wife."

And Moses lifted the rod out of the ground as easily as if it had been stuck loosely into sand.

The Five Books of Moses

The story which tells how Moses went back to his birthplace to free his people from slavery is the most memorable chapter in the long history of the Jews.

When Moses led his people out of Egypt he took them

to Mount Sinai and there dedicated them to a code of laws which has since received recognition by half of mankind. The books in which the teachings of Moses are recorded, are known as The Five Books of Moses, and are called the Torah — the most sacred of all the Jewish sacred books.

The essence of these teachings are in the Ten Commandments.

The Ten Commandments, Moses was told on Mount Sinai, is the Law of Mankind; and any man, anywhere, who keeps these commandments is equal in the eyes of God to the most faithful of high priests.

According to legend, Moses lived one hundred and twenty years: forty in Egypt; forty in Midian; and forty leading his people from slavery to freedom; from Goshen to Canaan.

One great tragedy befell Moses at the close of his life: he came to the end of his days just before his people, under new leadership, were about to cross the Jordan River, and enter their Promised Land.

Moses blessed his people and left them to walk up to the top of Mount Abarim. And that was the last time his people saw him.

But they have never forgotten him. They, and their children, and an endless chain of generations of children, remember Moses, the Prophet of Prophets.

There is much in the life of Moses to remember. He was born in slavery and raised as a prince. He distinguished himself as a warrior in his youth; and was condemned to die for murder soon afterwards. For many years he lived in Midian as a fugitive from justice. He appeared in Egypt with his brother Aaron to emancipate his enslaved people. He led them through a hostile desert for forty years, and in the end he brought them within sight of the Promised Land.

Yet it is not because of any of these events that Moses is so well remembered. He is remembered because he gave to the world two tablets of stone on which were inscribed the Ten Commandments — summing up a code for men to live by.

And if men were to live by that code, this world would be a very good world to live in.

IX. DAVID: The Immortal Singer

The Fearless Shepherd

There was a weaver of sacred carpets in the city of Bethlehem whose name was Jesse. He married a girl named Nazbat and, in the course of many years, they had eight sons and two daughters. As their family increased, so increased their wealth. Jesse acquired flocks of sheep and grazing lands beyond Bethlehem; and he left the care of his flocks to his growing children.

The youngest of the family was named David.

The sons of Jesse disliked their youngest brother. And there were many reasons for their feelings. There was a great discrepancy in age between them, for when David was born, his oldest brothers were already grown men. And too, unlike any of his brothers, David was slender as a doe and swift as a swallow; his skin was fair and his hair was red. He had inherited great beauty. Because he was the youngest in the family, he was the favorite of his parents and his sisters; and he had been named "David" — which means beloved.

After his first day alone tending a flock of sheep on the slopes of the hills, David came home with tales of adventure such as none of the others had encountered. In each he told of performing feats of strength and acts of courage beyond the strength and courage of any ordinary man.

Naturally his brothers did not like David. They were glad when they grew old enough to join the armies of King Saul and to leave their young brother behind to tend his father's sheep. That pleased David, too. For he loved to be alone with the sheep, observing the heavens, playing endlessly on his *kinnor*, a small ten-stringed harp, and making up little songs through the long quiet hours.

His songs were like prayers. And he often prayed for adventure. The more tedious tasks came by day; the more dangerous and exciting, by night. For when he had gathered together the flock for the night, the young shepherd remained on guard against desert thieves, and against wolves, bears, and mountain tigers.

Often days and nights passed in succession without anything happening. But sometimes marauders came. Wolves howled. Mountain lions leaped out of the black night like threatening flame. David, so he later related, met danger with strength and courage, for God was with him.

Once four hungry lions and three ferocious bears swooped down upon his flock, and David, without weapons other than the stones of the field, killed them all and lost not a sheep or a lamb. Out of the skin of one of the lions he made a cloak for himself and he showed it around and kept it all the days of his life in remembrance of his battle with the wild beast. In the exultation of this victory, he sang:

Blessed is the man who does not walk in the counsel of the wicked, nor stands in the footsteps of the sinners! He shall be like a tree planted by the river: bringing forth its fruit in season, and its leaves never wither. And everything he shall undertake, shall prosper.

The Secret Visit

One day an old man came to Jesse's house in Bethlehem, carrying a long horn filled with sacred oil. It was the aged Prophet Samuel, and he said at once to Jesse:

"You must take an oath to keep secret what transpires in your house today!"

"What is wrong?" asked Jesse in alarm. "Is the king not well?"

"The king is well," said the prophet. "But he has offended the Lord, and therefore the Kingdom of Israel shall not go to Saul's offspring, but to another."

"Why are you here?" asked Jesse.

"I have been sent to anoint a son of yours, who is to inherit Saul's throne."

Jesse called his sons together, and the prophet held the anointing oil over the head of Eliab, Jesse's oldest son. But the sacred oil would not flow out of the horn. The prophet then held the oil over the head of Abinadab, Jesse's second son, and again the oil would not flow. Next came Shammah and Nathaniel and Raddai and Ozem, and each time the oil refused to flow from the horn.

Finally Samuel asked: "Have you still other sons?"

"I have another," said Jesse, "but he is the youngest and a mere child, who tends my sheep in the hills."

"Send for him," said the prophet.

When David arrived, all out of breath, the prophet arose from the circle of the family and held the oil over the boy's head. And the stream of sacred oil flowed freely, and as the drops fell upon the the shepherd's cloak they turned into pearls.

Then all knew that David had been chosen to be King of Israel after Saul's days were fulfilled. But they buried the secret in their hearts.

Each returned to his task. And David went up to the hills beyond Bethlehem to tend his father's flocks.

Encounter with Goliath

Not long after the prophet's visit to their home, Jesse sent his youngest son with provisions for his brothers in the army, encamped near Azekah. David found his brothers, and all the others in King Saul's army, downcast in the shadow of defeat before the Philistines with whom they were warring. For the Philistine giant, Goliath, had challenged King Saul to send a man to meet him in single combat and to let the war be determined by the outcome of that contest. And Saul had not a single man who could take up the challenge.

"I would meet him in combat," said David to his brother Eliab. "And I would surely put Goliath along with the chaff that the wind blows away."

"You?" shouted the ill-tempered Eliab. "You'd better run home to Mother's apron strings and to tasks befitting a boy!"

David left his brother, shamed by the angry words. But he spoke to other soldiers of his willingness to fight Goliath, and his certainty of victory.

Word reached King Saul that Jesse's youngest son, a mere stripling, without skill in battle, spoke with eagerness of his wish to fight the giant, and with great confidence that he could defeat the Philistine. The king sent for the red-haired boy and questioned him.

"The Lord is my shield," David answered. "I do not fear ten times ten Goliaths. Our adversaries may laugh to see one not yet of man's estate come to meet the dread Goliath; but the glory of our army will then be greater when I slay him and lower him into the dust."

David argued long before the king would give his consent. But finally King Saul sent word to the Philistines that he accepted Goliath's challenge and was sending a man to meet him in battle.

At the appointed hour and the appointed place, in the

valley between the camps of the two armies, Goliath appeared, the mightiest man then living on earth. He was six cubits and a span in height (9 feet, 9 inches), and his armor weighed five thousand shekels in brass. And he walked with giant strides, his great sword unsheathed and gleaming in the sun, ready for the encounter.

Suddenly he stopped, rooted to the spot, his unbelieving eyes fixed on his challenger: a slender boy not fully three cubit and one span in height, dressed in a shepherd's skin, wearing no breastplates and carrying no weapons, only a shepherd's sling and a shepherd's pouch over his right shoulder.

As the boy drew nearer, eyes fixed on Goliath, he took out a smooth stone, which he had found in a brook, and placed it in his sling.

"Am I a dog that you come at me with stones?" Goliath shouted, his voice resounding like thunder in the hills. "Come and I will feed you to the scavengers of field and sky."

"Curse on, as long as you have breath," said David. "Your trust is in your sword. But mine is in the Lord."

David let the stone fly from his sling, and it pierced Goliath's forehead.

The great warrior uttered an anguished cry and fell face forward into the dust of the ground.

While the armies of King Saul shouted with joy, and the armies of the Philistines, with dismay, David walked over to the fallen giant, took Goliath's sword from his cold hand, then cut off his head to complete the Philistines' humiliation.

Then David returned to his father's home and to his flocks in the hills. Alone at night he looked at the stars and thought of Goliath's end. He strummed his little ten-stringed harp and sang:

> *When I consider the heavens, the work of Your fingers, when I consider the moon and the stars which You have ordained, I wonder: What is man that You are mindful of him, and the son of man that You are concerned with him?*

The Fugitive

After David had killed Goliath and the Philistine armies were routed, King Saul became uneasy. For his own early exploits in battle were forgotten and the name of young David was on everyone's lips; particularly on the lips of the women, who admired David's comeliness as much as his valor.

"If I invite David to serve me and keep him always beside me," thought the jealous king, "his favor will diminish."

He sent for David and asked him to become the king's armor-bearer. When David arrived at the palace in his shepherd's attire, the king's son, Jonathan, bestowed upon Jesse's son his outer robe and his girdle and his sword —

which was a sign not only of great honor but of even greater affection. And after that day David and Jonathan were tied by a bond of affection and friendship greater than either had felt for his brothers. Then Saul's youngest daughter saw David, and she fell deeply in love with him. And the love of Saul's children for David only the more increased the king's resentment and jealousy.

Though David showed only reverence and loyalty to the king, distrust continued to corrode Saul's peace of mind. He brooded about it. He dared not let David out of his sight, suspecting his every move. And he feared to fall asleep when David was near him, for he had nightmares in each of which the young armor-bearer tried to kill the king and take the throne away from him.

Once King Saul awoke from one of these nightmares and threw his javelin at young David sitting at his feet. The weapon missed its mark, and David escaped to the hills.

Then began a long period in which David sought new hiding places, with the king's men following closely behind. David hid with priests and with kings, with shepherds, and in desert caves. By day he lay in hiding, and by night he traveled stealthily, always on the alert for his pursuers.

One day he hid in the lair of a wild beast. He rested on the bare ground in the shadows looking out of the cave through the narrow opening on the sunlit desert. A spider swung itself across the mouth of the cave and began weaving its web. David's first impulse was to destroy the creature, for he disliked spiders. But he dared not move forward, in fear of being detected. He lay there watching the busy insect and wondering why God had created spiders. Though there seemed to be a reason for everything under the sun, David could not think of any reason for the ugly little spider. He thought and thought about it until he fell asleep.

The sound of voices awakened David. And he heard someone say:

"David must have come this way."

"No, he cannot be hiding here," he heard another voice say, "for the entrance is covered with a spider web. No one has been here for a long time."

When the soldiers left, David recalled his thoughts about spiders, and he sang softly:

O Lord, my heart is not haughty nor my eyes lofty; neither do I exercise myself in matters or in things too high for me.

Shepherd into King

David lived all his life as if on borrowed time. It leaves one breathless just to enumerate all the stirring events in his life and his many accomplishments.

He killed the giant Goliath and earned the gratitude of his nation.

He became a great musician and a sweet singer.

He married a king's daughter; and then he married ninety-eight others.

He became king and reigned for forty years.

He united the Jewish kingdom.

He acquired Jerusalem.

He planned the building of the Temple.

He transferred the Ark with great pomp and festivity to the City of David.

And as king he went out in battle against the Philistines, the Moabites, the Ammonites, the Syrians, the Edomites, and many others.

Yet it is not because of any of these events and accomplishments that David is remembered.

The Songs of David

In spite of all the adventures in his life, David found time, particularly as he grew older, to write down the songs in his heart and the hymns he had composed. He wrote one hundred and fifty in all, some only a few lines long.

Yet this slender collection of songs has given comfort and joy to more people in the world than any other book of poems ever written. Its phrases have become part of a thousand languages and dialects in every section of the globe. Though people may not know their origins, they constantly use expressions borrowed from this book. These songs were sung in the Temple of Jerusalem in the days of King Solomon; and they are sung today in synagogue and church on practically every occasion of joy or sorrow.

In time of great triumph, people sing: *The stone which the builders rejected is become the chief cornerstone; this was the Lord's doing!*

And in the presence of death and bereavement, they chant: *As for man, his days are as grass; as the flower in the field, so he flourishes. For the wind passes over it, and it is gone; and the place thereof shall know it no more.*

Through generation after generation people have memorized these poems, and the beauty of the words has increased in luster with the passing of the centuries. And millions of children, before they have learned to read, have learned to say: *The Lord is my shepherd; I shall not want. He maketh me to lie down in green pastures: he leadeth me beside the still waters. He restoreth my soul. . . .*

This small book of poems is known as the Psalms of David or The Book of Psalms or the Psalter.

And we remember David, not because he was a giant killer, or a mighty king, but because he was a great singer and because he wrote down the songs that were born in his heart.

X. JOHN: The Messenger

The Murder of John's Father

In the days of King Herod the Wicked, there lived a good priest in Jerusalem named Zacharias, and his wife Elizabeth. But though they had been married many years, they had no children.

One day Zacharias prayed in the Temple of Jerusalem:

"O God, my hair is white and my bones grow feeble with age, yet have I no son to succeed me, a son who would observe the Commandments and enter in the priesthood."

As he prayed, Zacharias heard an angel speak:

"Grieve no more, Zacharias, for you shall have a son and you shall name him John."

"Give me a sign that I shall really have a son!" Zacharias pleaded.

"This shall be your sign," said the angel. "From this hour until the hour your son is named you shall be able to speak in signs only."

Zacharias opened his mouth to thank the angel, but he could make no sound. And not until his son was born and named did his power of speech return.

The aged priest and his wife were happy with their son;

but their joy turned into sorrow before the child was old enough to speak his father's name. For Herod, warned that a child had been born who would bring about the king's downfall, issued a decree that all boys under two years of age in the kingdom were to be seized and killed.

The king's men came at once to Jutta, and to the house of Zacharias and Elizabeth, to seize the infant John. But they found no one at home. When Herod's men failed to find John anywhere in Jutta, they came to Zacharias in the temple and asked:

"Where have you hidden your son?"

"I am a servant of God," said the priest, "and I spend my days beside the altar. My son now dwells with his mother in the hill country. But where they are I do not know."

The men reported the priest's answer to Herod, and he sent them back a second time with the message:

"If you do not turn over your son to my men, your blood will be upon your own hands."

"The Lord is my witness that my blood is innocent, and it shall be upon the hands of him who spills it."

The enraged king sent a guard to the temple at dawn, when there would be no one to see them, and ordered Zacharias to be killed wherever he was found.

The next morning the priests arrived in the temple and waited for Zacharias to lead them in prayer. But Zacharias did not appear. After waiting for a long time, one of them ventured into the inner chamber of the temple; and there, on the steps of the altar, he found Zacharias dead, his head lying in a pool of blood.

The priest rent his clothes in grief and ran out to tell the others what had happened. But when they entered the chamber of the altar, the body of Zacharias had disappeared, and his blood upon the steps had turned into stone and could not be wiped away.

John and His Teacher

Elizabeth fled into the hills to seek shelter for her son, but she could find none. The despairing mother cried out:

"O Dweller on High, give refuge to a mother and child unjustly pursued by a tyrant!"

At that moment, the hill upon which Elizabeth stood opened up like a gate to let the mother and child enter. Then the hill closed again. And there, nourished by a fountain and bread from heaven, Elizabeth and her son dwelt in safety for seven years.

On the seventh year Elizabeth led her son out of their hiding place and took him to the Hermit of Engedi, who dwelt in the Cave of David. This Hermit of Engedi was the Sage Matheno, respected for his learning and wisdom, who had come to the Cave of David to spend his days in meditation.

Elizabeth said to Matheno: "You are wise, Master

Matheno, and you are learned. Will you take my fatherless boy and teach him so that he will not grow up ignorant and without understanding?"

The boy found favor in Matheno's eyes, and the hermit replied: "Leave your son with me, and I shall teach him whatever little I know."

And after that day John remained with the Hermit of Engedi. They lived on wild fruit and nuts, and on the wild honey and carob pods that were abundant in the desert. Their clothes were few. And the cave was their dwelling place. All their waking hours they spent in study.

Elizabeth came to visit her son from time to time; and at each visit he seemed to have grown in stature and in knowledge. Each time his mother came, John told her of his love for the wise and gentle hermit.

Matheno did not teach John out of books. John would ask questions and Matheno would answer them. The teacher would demonstrate his answers with legends and parables.

One day Matheno explained to his young pupil why no strength is ever gained in idleness.

"Do not say, 'I did not seek, yet I found'; nor should you say, 'I sought but I did not find,' " said Matheno. "For they are not true. Say instead, 'I sought and I found.' For that is the truth."

Another day Matheno taught his young pupil the golden rule. And that, said Matheno, was: "Do not do unto others what you do not want others to do to you."

In that way their days passed, the pupil asking good questions, and the teacher giving wise answers.

The Messenger

John had been with Matheno for five years when Elizabeth died. John was twelve years old and wise beyond his years, but he grieved for his mother like a small child who could not be comforted. Matheno put his arm about John's shoulders and said:

"It is not well to weep because of death. For death is not the enemy of man; it is a friend who, when the work of life is done, cuts the cord that binds the human boat to earth, that it may sail away on smoother seas."

And after Elizabeth had been buried by her kin near Hebron, Matheno said to his pupil:

"There are no words that can describe a mother's worth. But it is selfishness that makes us wish to call again to earth those who have departed."

When time had healed John's wound and consoled him for his loss, Matheno said to him:

"John, you must now prepare yourself. For you have a mission."

"What is my mission?" asked John.

"You have been called the messenger who shall announce the coming of the Messiah."

"How shall I prepare myself?" asked John.

"There is but one way. Be pure in thought, in word, and in deed. And when the time comes, you will point the way to the Messiah."

"How am I to point the way?"

"The man who stands at the crossroads and points the way, but does not himself go that way, is no better than a block of wood that can serve the same purpose. The teacher must leave his footprints along the right path, so that those who come along in search of the road can see them and say: 'The Master went that way, and there we shall follow.' "

"And when they come to me what shall I do?" asked John.

"You must teach them how to purify their souls. And you must teach them by example. Wash your body before them, so that they may do the same. And as they cleanse their bodies, so shall they learn to cleanse their souls also."

"When shall I do that?" asked John.

"Now," said Matheno.

They went down together to the Jordan, east of Jericho, and there the hermit explained the inner meaning of the rite of baptism.

Two Heads on a Silver Charger

Word was brought to King Herod that John was ministering at the Jordan, and that he baptized his followers saying: "The hour of deliverance is at hand!" And the tyrant's heart was uneasy.

One day Herod was told that John had spoken harshly of the king's marriage to his brother Philip's wife, who called herself Herodias. The Baptist had proclaimed the marriage unlawful and called Herod and Herodias adulterers.

Herod at once had John arrested and brought before him. The king asked:

"Are you John, the son of Zacharias?"

"I am John, the son of Zacharias, whom your father murdered in the temple of God. And you are Herod, the lawless, son of Herod the Idumean, who multiplies sin in Israel."

"What sin do you speak of?" asked Herod, amazed that this man seemed fearless of temporal powers.

"The sin you know of in your heart. For you have caused your brother's wife to commit adultery with you in defiance of God's law."

Herod feared to harm the Baptist because of his great following, and desired to let him go. But Herodias longed for vengeance, and she demanded that John should be imprisoned in the dungeon of the fortress in Macheraus, near the Dead Sea. She ordered that he be flogged there and tortured, so that he might repent his words against her and Herod.

John suffered the torture and did not repent his words. Great multitudes of John's followers camped before the fortress, imploring Herod to let their leader go. But Herod stopped his ears and closed his heart to their pleas.

In the spring of that year, on his birthday, Herod gave a great feast for his nobles, and asked Salome, the beautiful daughter of Herodias by a former marriage, to dance before him and his guests. And when she had pleased him with her dance, Herod said:

"Ask of me whatever you desire, and it shall be given you."

Salome went to her mother's side and said: "You have heard Herod's promise. What shall I ask?"

"Ask for the head of John the Baptist," answered the wicked woman.

And Salome said to the king: "You have promised on your oath to give me whatever my heart desires. And my heart desires the head of John the Baptist on a silver charger."

At first Herod feared to do this. But Salome kept him to his oath, and he fulfilled her desire.

When the daughter of Herodias received the head of John the Baptist on a silver charger, she carried it to her mother. Then she ran out to exult on the ice pond which was contrived for her to dance upon. But as she reached the center of the pond, the ice opened beneath her and she sank into the water up to her neck. And no one was able to save her.

Herod ordered that they should bring the sword with which John's head had been cut off and with it cut off

Salome's head also. And they placed her head on a silver charger and carried it also to Herodias, her mother.

The queen looked upon the two heads and instantly her eyes lost their sight. She touched John's head, hoping to be cured of her blindness, but her hand withered like a dry leaf in a hot flame. She tried to cry out, but her tongue cleaved to her palate. Then they bound her with fetters to restrain her in her madness. And she spent the rest of her days in darkness and misery.

John's Bequest

We really know very little about John the Baptist. The legends about him are many; but the facts are few. Yet we seem to know him well.

For the few facts we know about him, justify him. And all the conflicting legends justify him.

He left no gospel or book of precepts or memorable sermons. Yet we feel that he left a great legacy — in the fact that he lived; and in the way that he lived.

XI. JESUS OF NAZARETH

Joseph the Carpenter

In the town of Bethlehem, in Palestine, there lived a carpenter, as wise as he was learned. His name was Joseph and, according to legend, when he was forty years old he married a neighbor's daughter named Escha. In time she bore him four sons and two daughters. The names of the sons were: Justus, Judas, Simon, and James; and the daughters are vaguely remembered as Esther and Tamar, or Anna and Salome, or Assia and Lydia, or something like that.

After forty-nine years of married life, with their children grown and some married, Escha died, leaving the old carpenter a widower at the age of eighty-nine.

The following year Joseph went up to Jerusalem, as he did each year, to celebrate one of the Jewish festivals. There, through a miraculous circumstance, he was entrusted by the priests with the guardianship of an orphan, a fourteen-year-old girl named Mary.

Joseph brought Mary home to Nazareth where he now lived, and left her in his home with companions her own age, whilst he went off to Capernaum and other towns to follow his work as a carpenter.

One day, while Joseph was away from home, Mary sat alone in her room working on a veil for the Temple of Jerusalem. Suddenly the room became filled with light and there entered a young man of ineffable beauty, an angel from heaven, and he said:

"Hail, Mary, full of grace, the Lord is with you!"

Then he foretold that she would have a son who would inherit the throne of David and would rule from sea to sea and to the ends of the earth.

Birth in a Cave

At that time the wicked King Herod had issued a decree that all his subjects must go to the towns of their birth to register in person for a census. Old Joseph placed young Mary on the family donkey, Thistle, and together with his two sons Simon and James, they started out from Nazareth in Galilee, far to the north, for Bethlehem six miles south of Jerusalem. The journey lasted for days.

Late one afternoon, as they came within three miles of their destination, Mary said:

"We must stop here, for my time has come. Go into the city and find me a midwife."

Joseph took Mary to a nearby cave and placed his two

sons to guard the entrance. Then he started out for Bethlehem.

On his way, Joseph suddenly noticed that although he was walking as quickly as he could, he remained always on the same spot.

He looked up at the sky and he saw the birds on wing suspended in mid-air without movement. Joseph turned his eyes to the laborers in the nearby field who were resting from the day's work and sitting at their evening meal. But they were not eating. The bread cutter was fixed in the act of cutting. The man who poured the drink was fixed in the act of pouring. And he who conveyed food to his mouth, did not convey it nor put it down.

On the hillside the sheep stood fixed in the middle of their steps. The shepherd, with upraised hand to urge them on, remained where he stood with upraised hand. By the river the lambs with outstretched necks, their mouths touching the water, were not drinking.

Everything in the world stood still.

Joseph lifted his eyes to the skies again. Suddenly there appeared a star, larger and brighter than any he had ever seen before. Nor had he ever seen a star in the shape of a woman with an infant in her arms and a crown of bright light upon the infant's head. As Joseph watched it in astonishment, the star began to move across the heavens until it came directly over the place where Mary rested in the cave. And there the star stopped.

The instant the star stopped, everything in the world began to move again. The birds continued on their flight. The laborers went on with their meal. The lambs at the river bank began to drink.

And Joseph hastened on his way.

Flight to Egypt

One day three Magi of the East, each a king in his own right, arrived in Jerusalem from distant Asshur. One of them was Melchior, an old man, fair-skinned, with white hair and a long white beard, and he carried thirty pieces of gold. The second was Jaspar, a youth of twenty with a reddish complexion, who carried rare incense. And the third was Balthasar, a dark-skinned middle-aged man with a black beard, who carried fragrant myrrh. Between them, the three kings represented all races and all ages of mankind. And they came into the market place, asking:

"Where is the child that was born to be king of the Jews? For we have seen his star in the East and have come bearing gifts and to worship him."

Rumor swiftly carried the news of the Magi to the ears of King Herod. He summoned them before him and said slyly to them:

"Go and find this child you seek. And when you find him bring him to me that I, too, may worship him."

But the Magi saw into the king's heart. They went to the child and his mother in the cave, and placed their gifts before the infant, whom they worshiped. Then they returned to their country without leaving a trace behind them.

King Herod waited a long time for the Magi to return. Finally he realized that he had been outwitted, and he issued a decree that all male infants in his realm should be slain, so that the baby the Magi had come to worship would surely perish, and none would remain to claim the kingdom of the Jews.

The very night that Herod issued his decree, Joseph the Carpenter was warned in a dream to go to Egypt with Mary and her child, Jesus, and remain there until a sign was given them to return.

Joseph awoke with a start, and long before dawn he and Mary and her child were on their way to the land where their people had once lived in slavery and where they now enjoyed freedom.

The wonders of that journey and the miracles performed by Jesus during the two years they remained in Egypt, if related one after the other, would challenge in length the Mahabharata.

By the touch of Jesus' swaddling-cloth, the dying were revived and made well. The touch of his hand, the sound of his voice, the glance of his eye, caused the dumb to speak, the deaf to hear, the blind to see, and the lame to walk straight. Idols tumbled in the temples when he appeared. And the possessed were freed of the evil spirits and demons within them.

Jesus Before Pharaoh

Word of the miracles wrought by the infant Jesus reached the ears of Pharaoh, ruler of Egypt. He was alarmed by the news, remembering Moses, many generations earlier, and ordered Joseph and his family to appear before him as soon as they reached Memphis, the capital of the kingdom.

Jesus was two years old when he was brought with his parents before the mighty ruler. He stood in front of his mother with a stalk of lilies in his hand. And the king addressed himself, not to Joseph or to Mary, but to the child.

"Another Hebrew boy, named Moses, came to our kingdom many generations ago, and he brought us much suffering. Are you not like Moses?"

"I came after Moses as the dawn comes after the night," said Jesus in a clear voice. "I bring neither anger nor vengeance. Wherever I go, gardens will grow where only nettles grew before."

And Pharaoh said: "I see you have a wand in your hand. Moses had a wand that turned the water in our rivers and our wells into blood for seven days. Will you do the same with your wand?"

Jesus stretched out his hand and waved the lilies toward the river; and the waters of the river turned into sweet milk.

Then Pharaoh asked: "Next time you stretch out your hand, will the land be filled with frogs and the dust with lice, as it was in the days of Moses?"

Jesus waved the lilies in his hand and the air became filled with seeds which the brisk breeze scattered over the fields to make them fertile.

And Pharaoh said once again: "If you can cause good seed to fly over our fields, will you also cause us to be plagued with flies, as our ancestors were plagued in the days of Moses?"

Jesus again waved his lilies as if they were a wand, and the air became filled with buzzing bees that gathered in swarms on the branches of trees, and they built many hives and the land was made rich with wild honey.

"There is your answer," said Jesus.

But the king asked: "Will you, like Moses before you, plague our cattle in the field, and our horses, and our camels and our sheep with grievous murrain, so that they will not multiply and they will die?"

Jesus was tired and climbed up into his mother's arms. And while he rested, all the animals in Egypt brought forth young.

Still Pharaoh was not reassured. He said to Jesus: "Will you scatter the ashes of our fires and cause man and beast to be covered with boils, and bring great sickness upon the land?"

Jesus uttered a word, and all those who suffered from illness in Egypt on that day were instantly cured.

"Will we be threatened with hail that will destroy our crops and ruin our fruit trees?" asked Pharaoh.

Jesus pointed his stalk of lilies into the air. And hail began to fall. It fell gently, and each hailstone clung to the trees like a rosebud. Then came thunder that tilled the fields. And the entire land of Egypt prospered.

"Of all the plagues of Moses," said Pharaoh, "the people remember the locusts with greatest horror. The locusts came in like dark clouds, and settled upon the ground. And when they rose, not a blade of grass nor a green leaf remained in all the land. Will you bring this plague upon us?"

Jesus waved his hand, and the air became filled with birds of many colors. They nested in the trees and filled the air with song.

"I know," said Pharaoh. "You plan to plague us with darkness so thick that it may be touched with the hand, and no man could see another, nor take one step in safety."

"I bring you light, not darkness," said Jesus. And, behold, the land was filled with a brightness unknown before, so that even the caverns, where there had never been any light, were now as bright as a field in the noonday sun.

"There is one last question," said the king. "What of the first-born in Egypt? Will the Angel of Death come, as he came in the days of Moses, and gather them, from the first-born of the king to the first-born of the handmaiden; yet shall he pass over the houses in which dwell your people?"

"The first-born shall live and they who are dead shall live," said Jesus. And in that moment all the first-born in Egypt who were in their graves arose and were happy.

Tears of joy rolled down the face of the ruler of Egypt. And he welcomed Joseph and his family to Memphis, inviting them to live there as long as they pleased.

Life on Marmion Way

When Herod died, Joseph and his family returned to Nazareth from Egypt. The old carpenter went back to his trade. In back of his house on Marmion Way he worked in his carpentry shop, for he was too old to travel about the countryside in search of work. In fact, Joseph was now so old that he could scarcely work at all, and depended on the help he received from little Jesus who came into the shop each workday. For Joseph had discovered that if a board was too short, he would hold one end and Jesus would bring it to the required length by pulling out the other end; and if the board was too long, Jesus shortened it by pushing the board in. Whatever the task that needed to be done, the boy accomplished it by the touch of his hand. And in that way, Joseph could carry out his commissions as a carpenter.

Often Jesus went out to play with the children of Nazareth, and they always recognized him as their leader. They also feared him, for he could make clay birds at the river's edge and then command them to fly away; and the clay birds flew away. Or he could carry hot coals for his mother's fire in the hem of his cloak and the garment did not burn. And sometimes he would say strange things that made them sad, though they did not know what he meant.

One day he was playing in a courtyard with a group of boys. And when they had finished their game some of the mothers called to the children and asked:

"If you could make a wish, what would you like to be when you grow up?"

"I would like to be a dyer," said one, the son of a mason. "For I love bright colors and I would dye the wool gay red and yellow and purple."

"I would like to be a jeweler," said another, "for I like the sparkling jewels and, also, they would make me rich."

"I would like to be a soldier," said the son of the miller, "for then I would wear a soldier's garb, and everyone would fear me."

"And I would like to be a sailor," said the shoemaker's son, "for then I would sail over the seas to many strange lands and have many great adventures."

"I love honey," said the well-digger's son, "so I would like to be a beekeeper. Then I could eat all the honey I want."

And the smallest of them said: "I would like to be a doctor, for then I would heal all that are sick and I would become famous."

"What would you like to be, son of Mary?" the women asked Jesus.

"I know what I will be," he answered. "I will be King of the Jews; and all the nations of the earth will worship me."

The women laughed and asked: "And what will your throne be made of, can you tell us? Will it be made of gold, or of silver, or of ivory?"

"None of these," said Jesus. "My throne will be made of wood. And if you come with me I will show you the tree from which it will be made."

He led them to a brook nearby and pointed to a young oak growing at the edge of the bank.

"There is the tree from which will come my throne," said Jesus. And he began to cry.

And none could understand why he wept.

Jesus Before Rabbi Levi

At the age of five years every boy in Nazareth was taken to Rabbi Levi to be instructed in the Letters and the Law. And Jesus, after his fifth birthday, was also taken by Joseph and Mary to the school. But Jesus did not remain there very long.

For when he was brought before the learned rabbi, the kindly old teacher said to Jesus:

"My son, can you repeat after me aleph?"

"I know aleph and beth and gimel, and the names of all the other letters in the alphabet," answered Jesus.

"Go on," said the amused teacher.

"I also know the meaning of the shapes of the different letters, for each shape has its meaning," Jesus continued. "I know why some letters are straight and others oblique; why some have points and others have none; why some have double figures and appear different when they are at the end of a word than when they come elsewhere. Do you want me to go on?"

"Go on, my son," said the astonished rabbi.

"Each letter, from aleph the first to tov the last of the twenty-two letters, has a special meaning of its own. And there is a reason why each letter is in its given place in the order of appearance."

"Go on, go on," said the amazed Rabbi Levi.

Jesus then explained the meaning of each letter and the reason for its place in the alphabet. He went on to explain that the letters of every important word give a clue to its inner meaning. And he ended with:

"The word *amt* [the Hebrew word for truth, pronounced ameth] consists of a (aleph), m (mem) and t (tov) — the first, the middle, and the last letters of the alphabet. This is intended to show that truth rests on a firm foundation and that it shall endure forever."

Now Jesus was silent again and the old Rabbi Levi looked at him with awe and reverence for some time. Finally he turned to Joseph and Mary and said:

"I believe this boy must have been born before Noah to have gained so much knowledge. Take him home. For I thought you brought me a pupil, but instead you have brought me a master."

And Jesus did not return to school again.

Jesus in the Temple

When Jesus was twelve years old, he went up with his family and their kin and their neighbors to celebrate the Feast of the Passover in Jerusalem, as was customary.

And after the feast the pilgrims streamed back from Jerusalem to their homes in all parts of Judea. The men traveled in groups; the women preceding them in separate companies. Joseph, in the company of his sons and kin, did not see Jesus around, but he assumed that the boy was with Mary, and the women of the household. And Mary, who did not see Jesus, assumed that he was with Joseph, and the men of Nazareth.

After a day's journey from Jerusalem, Joseph's family gathered for the evening meal, and Jesus was not among them. Joseph and Mary and all the members of the family began to seek him among their kin and neighbors. With mounting anxiety they went from camp to camp, asking:

"Have you seen our boy, Jesus?"

But no one had seen him all day long.

Then Joseph said to Mary: "No one has seen Jesus since

we left Jerusalem. Let us return to the temple and seek him there."

They returned to the temple the next day, and there they found a great assembly of the learned priests and teachers questioning a young boy before them on the mysteries of the Law and the Sayings of the Prophets.

The boy before the learned assembly was their son Jesus.

One old rabbi asked him: "What can you tell us of the spiritual kingdom that the Messiah will establish?"

And the boy replied: "The world was created in six days, each day representing a millennium. Just as at the end of six days comes the Sabbath, so also at the end of six thousand years from the days of Adam, the world will come to an end and the Messiah will arrive. And the Messiah, son of David, will reign forever." Then Jesus explained that that kingdom will be like the kingdom of the ten lost tribes beyond the Sambatyon River, where all the people live in justice and peace.

The learned men turned in astonishment and asked of each other: "Pray, who can this boy be?"

An astronomer was present in the assembly at the temple, and he arose and asked Jesus:

"What do you know about astronomy?"

Jesus, without hesitating or faltering, explained the number of spheres and the heavenly bodies, and the meaning of their numbers; he expounded on their different natures and operations; he gave the motion of the planets each day, and each hour of the day; and he ended with a commentary on the intrastellar mysteries beyond the reach of reason.

A physician skilled in the natural sciences arose in the assembly and asked Jesus:

"Have you studied medicine and the related sciences?"

And Jesus enumerated the members of the body and their functions; the number of the bones, veins, arteries, and nerves, and all the intakes and outlets of the body; he explained the effects of heat or dryness on the human body, or heat and cold; and the disturbances created in the body by variations of moisture and temperature. From the physical body of man he passed over to the soul and its powers, with a discourse on the relationship between soul and body, beyond the reach of any mortal mind.

The assembly in the temple were still discussing all the things Jesus had said, when Mary came forward, saying:

"My son, your father and I sought for you everywhere with troubled hearts. What have you eaten these last two days?"

"The teachers in the temple bade me share their bread," said Jesus, "and they would not let me go hungry."

Then the family returned to Nazareth together.

Jesus was thoughtful all along the way, and when they reached home, he said to his mother:

"The rabbis think that God has favorites among the sons of men and that the Jews are his favorite children. But I cannot see how God can have favorites and remain just. Do the flowers grow only on this side of the walls of Jerusalem? Are the seasons of seeding and reaping only for the

Jews? It seems to me that all the children of God are greatly blessed. When I grow a little older, it is my wish to go out into the world and meet with my kin in other lands."

The Nobleman and His Sons

There are some strange legends about the travels and adventures of young Jesus in many lands. According to one remarkable story, Prince Ravanna of Orissa invited him to come to India to study Brahminism in the temple of Vishnu. Jesus went to India and for four years studied the Vedas and the Upanishads, and other sacred works of Brahminism. He found much that he liked in them, but he was distressed by their teachings of the caste system.

And he told the people the Parable of the Nobleman and His Unjust Sons, to illustrate that he who does not believe in the equality of man cannot believe in the justice of God:

There was a certain nobleman who owned a great estate. He had four sons and he wanted them to grow strong by the talents they possessed. He called them together and gave each his share of the great wealth, then bade them leave and prosper.

The oldest son, who was very shrewd and selfish, called his younger brothers to him one by one. To the eldest of the three he said: "Let us not divide our wealth. Let me, instead, be your priest and leader, and you become the king and ruler." And he gave the brother a sword with which to defend the estate.

To the second brother he gave the right to graze flocks upon the land and the right to use the soil for crops.

There was nothing left to give the youngest brother, so he was put in chains and commanded to serve the older brothers as a slave.

After some time the nobleman came to see how his sons had fared. When he saw what had happened, he placed the priest in prison, he flung the king and his crown into the dust; and he upbraided the farmer for failing to rescue the youngest brother from slavery. Then the father found his youngest son and with his own hands broke the cruel chains of slavery and set him free.

When the sons repented of the wrong they had done, the father again divided his estate among them. And the brothers promised to live thereafter in peace and equality.

This parable, and other parables like this, Jesus preached as he traveled through the land.

The Sermon on the Mount

The events in the life of Jesus from the time he came to the Jordan in his twenty-ninth year to be baptized by John, to the time he was crucified on the Hill of the Skulls, is known throughout the world.

Today, the teachings for which he was crucified are

accepted by over six hundred million people, in many lands.

The legends about Jesus, and particularly the legends of the miracles he performed, are many. But Jesus is remembered with love throughout Christendom not for the many miracles which everyone loves to hear and relate at one time or another, but for his teachings and sayings.

The essence of what he taught is to be found in the Sermon on the Mount, and in the parables in the Gospels.

And more than all the lore that has accumulated about Jesus, the people remember one sentence spoken at the Last Supper, when Jesus knew that he would be with his disciples only a little while longer. And he said to them:

"*By this shall all know that you are my disciples — if you have love for one another.*"

XII. MOHAMMED: Messenger of Allah

The Year of the White Elephant

Between the Red Sea and the Persian Gulf sprawls a wasteland known as the Island of the Arabs. It is a country, in area seven times the size of France, in population less than the city of New York, and in climate, for the most part, the cruelest on earth.

According to legend, when the world was created Allah divided evenly throughout the earth the mountains and the rivers, the valleys and the seas, the good grazing land and the poor rocky earth. Then Allah decided to give each land a measure of sand. And he commanded the Angel Gabriel to take a sack of sand and pour some upon each part of the newly created earth.

As Gabriel went on his way down to earth, he was followed by Satan, who ripped the sandbag on the angel's back, and the sand spilled out all in one spot. The sand absorbed the water of the seas and the rivers of the land where it fell, and created a dreadful desert. That desert was Arabia.

Ever since then the land of Arabia has been parched. The sun by day beats down on the yellow sand, and all that lives suffers from thirst; at nightfall the bitter cold turns the dew on the sand dunes into frost and chills the tent-dwellers to the marrow of their bones.

And water — not oil, not gold, not iron ore, but water — is the treasure men seek. Wherever a spring was found, that place became holy ground; and where the flow of the spring was constant, that was the site of a holy city.

There was such a spring not very far from the Red Sea, and around it grew up the sacred city of Mecca. The spring of Mecca is no ordinary spring, but the never-failing Zemzem.

According to the Arabs, many, many centuries ago, when the child Ishmael and his mother, Hagar, were driven from his father's house into the desert, they were about to perish from thirst. Ishmael kicked the hot sand with his toe, and from that spot a well gushed out and saved them.

When his father, Abraham, heard about the miracle and came to see the place, he discovered that the miraculous well, the Zemzem, was near the spot where Adam and Eve had lived after they had been expelled from the Garden of Eden. There Abraham and his son Ishmael erected a temple and named it the Kaaba. And around the well and the temple grew up the city of Mecca.

Mecca has been regarded as a sacred city ever since. Caravans from many lands came to Mecca. Merchants flourished. The city grew. And whoever had control over the Zemzem waters and the Kaaba had great power and wealth, and became the envy of all neighboring rulers.

In the city of Sana, in the neighboring land of Yemen, the envious Abyssinian ruler Abraha, a Christian by conversion, decided to turn the great caravans and the wealth they brought with them, from Mecca to Sana. He built great marble churches with golden cupolas, and turned Sana into a city of wonders.

But the people of the desert seemed little impressed with Abraha's accomplishments and mocked his churches. Whereupon Abraha assembled a great army and, seated upon a huge white elephant, led his people to destroy the city of Mecca.

When the Meccans heard of Abraha's coming on a white elephant — an animal they had never heard of before — they fled in terror. Abraha, ruler of Yemen, marched unchallenged to besiege and conquer a deserted city.

Yet he never conquered it.

From the south, in the direction of the sea, there suddenly appeared a flock of sparrows so vast as to darken the skies. Each sparrow carried a small stone in its beak, and a stone in each claw. The sparrows emptied their stones upon Abraha and his host within sight of Mecca, and the would-be conqueror fled. And the white elephant knelt within view of the Kaaba and the Zemzem well.

The Arabs named that year The Year of the White Elephant. It is remembered because Allah performed a miracle to save the sacred city, Mecca, from the infidel Abraha.

And that year is also remembered because in the Year of

the White Elephant a child was born in Mecca, destined for greatness, who was named Mohammed.

The Falling Stars

Seven weeks less one day after the ruler of Yemen was vanquished by the sparrows, there was great rejoicing in heaven. Satan and his host of demons could hear the jubilation even in their regions of darkness.

"What could be the cause of this jubilation?" asked the demons.

"Let us sneak up to the Gates of Heaven," said Satan, "and find out."

Satan and the evil spirits attempted to come near the heavenly gates, but they were assailed by the archangels and their hosts with flaming torches. Satan and his demons were driven back down into their dark dwelling in the bowels of the earth.

The people on earth saw the torches flung by the angels, and they called them falling stars. But the sages knew the falling stars to be a sign that there was rejoicing in heaven over a great impending event.

That night the stars fell over Arabia like a downpour of heavenly sparks. The earth began to tremble and quake.

The mountains sang: "*There is no god but Allah!*"

And the valleys responded: "*And Mohammed is his Prophet!*"

In faraway Persia where the Eternal Fire of Zoroaster had been burning for centuries, the flame suddenly went out; and the pillars of the temples of Chosroes and Ctesiphon, beyond the Tigris River, crumbled into dust.

Countless other miracles took place all over the world, while on this night a young widow, deep in sorrow for her husband who had died soon after their wedding night, gave birth without pain to a child with a shining face.

As soon as the child was born, his mother Aminah (whose name in Arabic means "Faith") sent word to Abd Al-Muttalib, her father-in-law and a leader in Mecca. Muttalib, who was seventy years old, sat in the sacred enclosure of the Kaaba at the head of the principal men of his tribe when the news came to him that his son Abdallah's wife had given birth to a boy. He rose immediately and went to Aminah's home, followed by all his friends. There the grandfather tenderly lifted up the infant and carried him to the Kaaba to name the child before the altar.

"I name you," said the grandfather, "Mohammed the Praised! And you shall be known from this day forward as Mohammed ibn Abdallah, ibn Abd-al-Muttalib, ibn Hashim, of the Koreishite Tribe!"

Those present blessed the child. They recalled the wondrous display of falling stars when Mohammed was born; and all expected great things of him when he grew up.

Childhood in the Desert

Mohammed's mother belonged to the noble Koreish tribe, and it was not proper for her to nurse her child. She gave her son to a poor woman of the lowly tribe of the Banu-Saad, Halima by name, to take the child to the desert and care for him until he was weaned.

"The Mecca air is not good for an infant," said the mother to the Bedouin woman. "The desert air will make my son strong."

"The desert air, and my milk, will make your son strong," said Halima. And she added: "Only in the desert does one become an Arab."

The child Mohammed remained in the desert for two years, absorbing not only Halima's milk and the desert air, but also the customs and ways of the poor Bedouins in the desert waste. His eyes became accustomed to the sight of black tents and yellow sand; his nostrils became accustomed to the smell of sheep and camels; and from the flaps of the black tent each day he saw an unending emptiness, and the earth which appeared as if on the first day the world was created. And at night he saw the bright stars in an ocean of darkness, while the faint music of distant shepherds filled the air like a great longing.

At the age of two, Mohammed was weaned and brought back to his mother. She was so pleased with his growth and robustness that she allowed Halima to take him back to the desert for another two years.

Halima and her husband and the entire tribe of Banu-Saad Bedouins were delighted to have Mohammed back, for they had noticed many strange things about the child that pleased them. Their camels gave more milk when he was around; and their flocks suffered no illness. The sheep bowed when Mohammed came near. And wherever Mohammed went, there the grass grew. All these reasons made the poor Bedouins very glad to have Mohammed back in their camp.

One day, when Mohammed was four years old, something happened which disturbed Halima and her family:

Mohammed was out on the edge of the desert playing with Mesrut, Halima's son. Suddenly two angels in gleaming white robes came down from the skies. One was the Angel Gabriel, and the other was the Angel Michael. While Mesrut watched with astonishment, the angels gently bared Mohammed's breast. They took out his heart and pressed out the drop of sin with which every human being has been born since the days of Adam. Then they put the sinless heart back in its place and covered Mohammed's breast. And then the angels vanished as suddenly as they had appeared.

When word of this was brought to Halima and her husband by their son Mesrut, they at once met with the leaders of their tribe. And all agreed that the child must be taken back to his mother in Mecca, without delay.

Life with Grandfather

Aminah took her son to visit her parents and her kin in Yathrib. There she also took her son to the grave of his father, Abdallah. But after two years in Yathrib, Aminah longed to return to Mecca. And with her son and a maidservant she started out for the holy city. At a place called Al-Abwa, Aminah suddenly became ill and just as suddenly, died.

(Mohammed was only six years old then, but he remembered this sad event vividly all the days of his life. Nearly fifty years later he spoke with deep feeling about his mother's death, as if she had just died. He had gained fame as a Prophet, and his name was known by a thousand endearing appellations when he went to visit her grave at Al-Abwa. And he wept again like an orphan of six, exclaiming:

"This is my mother's grave! I sought leave to pray for her salvation, but my prayer was not granted!")

The orphaned Mohammed passed into the care of his aging grandfather. And the old man watched over his young grandson like the apple of his eye. Wherever Muttalib sat, Mohammed sat beside him; and wherever Muttalib went, Mohammed went with him.

The old man told his grandson all he remembered of the war with Abraha in all its details. He told about the time when he and his sons dug up two golden gazelles, and swords, and suits of armor, which had been buried by a king three centuries earlier; and how they shot arrows before the image of Hubal in the Kaaba to find out to whom the gold images and the armor should go; and the arrows decided that the gold should go to the Kaaba and the armor to Muttalib and his sons.

Often Muttalib told his grandson about Abdallah, whom the boy had never seen.

"It came about this way," the old man related. "I had prayed for many sons and I had vowed a sacred vow that if ten sons were given me I would sacrifice one of them to Hubal. Ten sons were given me and your father, Abdallah, was the youngest of the ten. I took my sons to the altar of the Kaaba. The name of each was inscribed on an arrow, and the lots were cast. And the lot fell upon Abdallah, your father."

Muttalib looked at his grandson from the corner of his eye, then continued:

"When I came to keep my vow, an angel stayed my hand. Then I did not know how to keep my vow and I was deeply troubled. But my daughters said: 'Cast the lots again between Abdallah and a hundred camels, and if the camels should be accepted as ransom for our brother, then you need have no scruple to spare your beloved son!' That was done and your father was spared. And all the citizens of Mecca feasted on that sacrifice!"

Muttalib spoke endlessly about Abdallah. And he sighed each time he mentioned the name of his youngest son.

"Your father was the most handsome young man in Mecca. And all the young maidens wanted to marry him. The night he married your mother, two hundred maidens died of love-sickness. But, alas, only three days after his wedding he went to Gaza, and we never saw him again. He died on the way and was buried in Yathrib."

Frequently the old leader of his tribe took his grandson to the market place filled with soothsayers, magicians, merchants, and beggars. The merchants displayed their wares. The smell of incense and perfume mingled with the odor of many animals. Camels with tinkling bells on their necks passed softly by. Strolling singers sought an audience that would offer some coppers. Food was sold. Slaves were sold. Many languages were spoken by people from many lands, in every kind of costume. Gambling games went on at every side. And everywhere men talked of religion.

Muttalib kept his grandson beside him and constantly explained all they saw and heard, and in that way taught him the truth of the world. Sometimes they went out into the market place at night, when the bonfires were lit in many places and the smoke went up in the chilling air to mingle with the many smells. And all the time Muttalib instructed the boy in the ways of his people.

Even in the sacred enclosure of the Kaaba, where Muttalib always sat apart on his carpet and none of his sons or the leaders of his tribe dared come too close, Mohammed was allowed to sit with him on his carpet.

Once, as Abd-al-Muttalib sat in the shadow of the

Kaaba, expounding on the history of the Black Stone in the Kaaba, which Adam had brought from the Garden of Eden, Mohammed came and sat down near his grandfather. The elders who sat a little distance from their leader, threatened to punish the boy for his lack of reverence, and were about to drive him away, but the old man said:

"Leave the child alone. By the God of my fathers, I swear that he will one day be a mighty prophet!"

Mohammed and His Uncle

Mohammed had just reached his eighth birthday, and nearing the time to enter school, when his grandfather died. And the orphan went to live with his uncle, Abu Talib.

In the histories about Mohammed they always present Abu Talib as a very good man. Yet in the stories about him he fails to live up to that reputation. Although he took his orphaned nephew and gave him food and shelter, he did not send him to school. Instead he assigned him to the stables to learn how to care for camels.

Abu Talib was a trader who made frequent trips to distant Yemen and Syria, and all his travels were made by camel. He owned a string of camels which he used for his caravan, and Mohammed was taught to care for the animals when they were at home in Mecca.

One day Mohammed begged his uncle to take him along on one of the journeys. Abu Talib consented. And the twelve-year-old boy started on his first exciting adventure. During the long days of travel his uncle told the boy about the cities they passed and the historic places they crossed, each usually marked by the memory of a great war.

Yet what stirred Mohammed's imagination most was not the new sights and the marvelous stories about them, but his first contact with the teachings of the Jews and the Christians when he reached Syria. And he tried to contrast what he had learned with what he knew of the faith of his own people.

He tried to learn on this journey how to be so helpful to his uncle that Abu Talib would never again leave him behind in Mecca. And after that trip, Mohammed was always beside his uncle on his travels.

Once during these journeys they met a monk named Bahirah. The monk talked with the boy Mohammed for some time. Then he turned to Abu Talib and asked:

"Will you allow me to examine this boy?"

Abu Talib granted the strange request. Bahirah looked at the boy's back, and pointing to a mole between the shoulders, he said:

"This is the sign I have been looking for. It is the sign of the Prophet that was foretold."

Mohammed remembered what his grandfather had said four years earlier, but he did not dwell on the sign and the prophecy. For he was soon involved in a war that had broken out between a Bedouin tribe and his kinsmen.

In this war Mohammed acted as his uncle's armor-bearer; and often himself engaged in shooting arrows at the enemy.

The war lasted a full year. But throughout the many battles Mohammed kept thinking of justice and injustice in the world, and the ideas of peace and love of one's enemy, that he had so often heard about in the market places of Syria. Throughout the war he heard his uncle and kinsmen appeal for help to their idols. And Mohammed wondered:

"How can the false deities which create nothing, but are themselves created give assistance to others? Have they feet to walk with? Or have they hands to lay hold with? Or have they eyes to see with? Or have they ears to hear with? They whom you invoke beside Allah cannot assist you!"

And the idea of a new religion for his people began to germinate in his mind. Once started, the idea grew like a seed well planted. And people began to notice that Mohammed was forever preoccupied.

Upon his return from the war, Mohammed became a shepherd in the hills around Mecca. He turned to herding sheep and goats and camels, for he had neither the talent nor the inclination to be a merchant. And he also chose this occupation because he considered it the occupation of a prophet.

(Later in life he exclaimed: *Verily there hath been no prophet raised up, who performed not the work of a shepherd.*)

In the solitude of the desert, performing the tasks of a shepherd, Mohammed thought of all the evils his eyes had seen in Mecca; and of all the reforms that were needed to bring his people closer to Allah, the One God.

The Memorable Flight

Many years were to go by before Mohammed would appear before his people and declare with certainty that he was a Messenger and a Prophet and an Apostle of God, sent to give his people and the world a new religion.

At the age of twenty-five he married a rich widow. The next fifteen years of his life he spent in meditation. He had not learned to read or write, but he had people read to him, particularly from the Old and the New Testaments. Then he would withdraw into a cave in the desert to meditate.

Mohammed finally confided to his wife, Kadijah, that the Angel Gabriel had come in a vision and read to him from golden tablets. Kadijah believed in her husband's visions and caused scribes to write down his revelations.

The Meccans scoffed at Mohammed and his sermons. In the first three years he won about forty converts, including his wife and the members of his immediate family. But slowly the fame of his sermons went out and the circle of his audience widened. When he began to gain many adherents, the Meccans plotted to kill him. The plot became known to Mohammed and he fled one night from Mecca to Yathrib, a city nearly three hundred miles away.

This flight from Mecca to Yathrib has since become one of the most important events in the history of Mohammedanism. It is known as Hegira, meaning "the flight." And Mohammedans count their time from A.H. or Anno Hegira, the Year of the Flight, which took place on the twentieth of September, 622 A.D. The name of the city to which Mohammed fled, Yathrib, was changed to Medina (Al Nabi) the city (or kingdom) of the Prophet.

At this time, according to the records, Mohammed was of middle height, lean, broad-shouldered, his head well proportioned, his black hair curly, his black eyes full of kindness but fierce when he was aroused. And his long black beard gave dignity to his appearance. He had a mole between his shoulders, which his followers said was his "seal of prophecy."

The Prophet was at once respected for the keenness of his mind, the simplicity of his living, his disgust with hypocrisy, and his unbounded sympathy for the poor. Above all he was respected by both friend and enemy for the singleness of purpose with which he recruited followers to his cause.

Mohammed organized the growing numbers of his followers into an army, and he returned to Mecca to convert the Meccans to his teachings at the point of a sword.

Green Flag of the Prophet

The teachings of Mohammed were gathered into a book of lessons, known as the Koran, which means "the lesson" or "the recitation." The Koran, along with the

Five Books of Moses, the Psalms, and the Gospels of the New Testament, became the Sacred Scriptures of his followers. But the Koran was held in highest esteem.

Their code of religious laws was simple at first. The drinking of any intoxicating liquor, the playing of games of chance, and the worship of images, were strictly forbidden. Daily prayers, the giving of charity, fasting on prescribed days, and a pilgrimage to Mecca, were the duties of every Moslem (True Believer).

During the Holy Wars engaged in by Mohammed, he announced that whoever died in defense of the faith would be considered a martyr. Thousands, then hundreds of thousands, swelled the ranks of the armies under the Green Flag of the Prophet. And these crusading armies marched east and west, north and south.

In the early centuries of the Mohammedan crusades, the Moslems carried with them Arabic philosophy, poetry, and Arabic science, particularly mathematics and medicine which, at that time, had reached a high state among them.

Today, the prophet who started out as a lowly shepherd has a following of over two hundred and fifty million people in Egypt, Iran, India, Pakistan, and in practically all parts of Asia and Africa.

Books to Read

Anyone who wishes to obtain more specific yet concise information on any topic touched upon in this book would do well to consult, topically, any one of the standard encyclopedias or those devoted to religion and ethics. Most libraries would have them.

But the reader wishing to explore this field more fully will find the choice of reading plentiful and varied. Here are several books that deal, in more or less popular form, with the material touched upon in this book:

AN INTRODUCTION TO THE STUDY OF SOME LIVING RELIGIONS OF THE EAST, by Sydney Cave; Duckworth, London, 1921.

Within a short space this good book presents: Hinduism, Zoroastrianism, Buddhism, the religions of China and Japan, and Islam. It gives their origins, their sacred writings, and their development to the present day. Not written for the layman, yet the layman and the young reader will find it very rewarding.

HOW THE GREAT RELIGIONS BEGAN, by Joseph Gaer; Dodd, Mead, New York, revised edition, 1950.

A concise review of how the great living religions arose, with a general indication of their basic tenets; presented mainly in story form.

GREAT PEOPLE OF THE PAST, by Rhoda Power; Macmillan, New York, 1932.

This book of brief biographies contains a good chapter on Gautama the Buddha ("The Beggar Prince"); another on Confucius ("The Wise Man of China"); and one on Mohammed ("The Prophet of Arabia"). It is written in a lively manner and with a twinkle in the author's pen, so to speak.

MYTHS AND LEGENDS OF INDIA, by J. M. Macfie; T. & T. Clark, Edinburgh, 1924.

Decidedly the best collection in English of Hindu legends taken from the Ramayana, the Mahabharata, and the Puranas. It is also an excellent introduction to the study of Hinduism.

SACRED TALES OF INDIA, by Dwijendra Nath Neogi; Macmillan, London, 1916.

Twenty popular tales of wonder, related presumably by priestly storytellers on the days devoted to certain Hindu gods and goddesses. These are given in traditional style. A good collection of Hindu folk legends, as they are presented to the young people of India.

HOLIDAYS AROUND THE WORLD, by Joseph Gaer; Little, Brown, Boston, 1953.

A popular presentation of the most important holidays throughout the world, given in a way to illuminate the religions treated, and stressing the lore.

THE MASTER MONKEY, by Dhan Gopal Mukerji; Dutton, New York, 1932.

This is a book about a monkey, unlike any other monkey in the world. General Hanuman is a monkey who served Rama, who was Vishnu in a previous incarnation, and Siva in his seventh incarnation. It sounds complicated as told here; but it becomes quite exciting when told by the master storyteller of India.

CONFUCIUS AND HIS QUEST, by Maurice Magree; translated by Eliot Fay; Thornton Butterworth, London, 1929.

A delightful fictionized biography of Confucius, written in folklore manner and based on authentic lore about Confucius.

CONFUCIUS AND TAOISM, by E. S. Bonsall; The Epsworth Press, London, 1934.

One of the Great Religions of the East studies by a distinguished scholar; brief, lucid, a good introduction to both of these religions of China. It contains a good bibliography for those who wish to explore the topic with thoroughness.

SAYINGS OF CONFUCIUS, by Lionel Giles; John Murray, London, 1912.

This little book, one of The Wisdom of the East series, gives a translation of the greater part of the Confucian sayings in the Analects of Confucius. The Introduction and the Notes are particularly good for their fairness and clarity.

THE LORE OF THE OLD TESTAMENT, by Joseph Gaer; Little, Brown, Boston, 1951.

This book presents the Old Testament story as it appears in folk imagination; contains many legends about Abraham, Moses, and David.

YOUNG KING DAVID, by Marian King; Lippincott, Philadelphia, 1948.

This fictionalized biography of King David captures the spirit of the man who started out as a lowly shepherd boy and died a great king; but is remembered because he was a poet and the author of the Book of Psalms.

THE BIBLE AND THE COMMON READER, by Mary Ellen Chase; Macmillan, New York, 1949.

A stimulating discussion of the poetic wealth to be found in the Bible, written with excitement. Reads like a novel and is far more rewarding. Should be read by everyone interested in the Bible as literature.

THE PRAISES OF ISRAEL, by John Paterson; Scribner's, New York, 1950.

A good study of the Psalter in terms of its contents and religious value.

THE LORE OF THE NEW TESTAMENT, by Joseph Gaer; Little, Brown, Boston, 1952.

The most recent collection of Apocryphal legends on the New Testament story, containing a large section of little-known legends about the youth of Jesus and his adventures in many lands.

THE GROWTH OF THE GOSPELS, by Frederick C. Grant; The Abingdon Press, New York, 1933.

Though intended for the student, this book by an eminent scholar is so lucidly written that any layman can read it with enjoyment and profit.

THE PARABLES OF THE SYNOPTIC GOSPELS, by B. T. D. Smith, Cambridge University Press, London, 1937.

An excellent study of the parable as a literary form, and its use as given in the Gospels.

THE STORY OF JESUS, by Walter Russell Bowie; Scribner's, New York, 1937.

This is a simple but stirring story of one so important to the Western world that with his birth people stopped, as it were, their record of time, and in wonder and admiration began to count all time from that day on: A.D.

JESUS OF NAZARETH, by Joseph Klausner, translated from the Hebrew by Herbert Danby; Macmillan, New York, 1925.

A great scholarly work, beautifully written, giving a clear insight into the times and conditions of the world in the days of Jesus.

LIFE OF JESUS, by Ernest Renan, translated from the French by Charles Edwin Wilbour; Carleton Publisher, New York, 1874. (There are a number of more recent editions, and almost any of them will do.)

One of the earliest of the many biographies of Jesus and still one of the best.

MOHAMMED, by Essad Bey, translated by Helmut L. Ripperger; Longmans, Green, New York, 1936.

A good biography of Mohammed, the man, the prophet, and the political leader. Gives a clear description of the conditions in Arabia in Mohammed's day, so that the rise of Mohammedanism can be better understood.

THE SHORT KORAN, edited by George M. Lamsa; Ziff-Davis, Chicago, 1949.

A book of ninety-one quotations from the Koran, arranged topically, beginning with Creation and ending with Hell and Torment, for the reader who wants to become casually acquainted with the Koran. Those wanting a fuller understanding of the Koran are advised to see the Koran as translated by J. M. Rodwell.

Acknowledgments

The numerous books on the living religions, their scriptures and their lore, which I have read over a period of many years, each have contributed something to the contents of this little book, but range over too wide a field to be listed here. I am especially indebted, however, for the two Jatakas: "The Talkative Tortoise" and "The Ass in the Lion's Skin" (originally appearing in Trübner's Oriental Series, 1880), which I have quoted from the introduction to the *Buddhist Birth-Stories*, translated by T. W. Rhys Davids.

The major part of the following sections: "Abraham: The Boy Who Discovered God"; "Moses: The Lawgiver"; "David: The Immortal Singer"; "John: The Messenger"; and "Jesus of Nazareth," are taken from or based on material in my earlier books, *The Lore of the Old Testament* and *The Lore of the New Testament*, and my thanks are due to Little, Brown and Company for their permission to use this material.

J. G.

Index